Olive: Response to Girdling, Micronutrients and Growth Retardants

THE AUTHORS

Dr. Amit Jasrotia is presently working as Junior Scientist (Fruit Science) at Regional Horticultural Research Sub-Station, Bhaderwah, SKUAST-Jammu and is engaged in research on temperate fruit crops. He has handled 4 institutional and 4 externally funded projects. He has published 35 articles in various national and international journals. He is a Life-member of 4 National Horticultural Societies of India.

Prof. V.K.Wali is presently working as Head, Division of Fruit Science and Director Research, SKUAST-Jammu. He has handled 12 institutional and 15 externally projects. Guided 13 M.Sc. and 09 Ph.D students. He has published 95 articles in various national and international journals. He is a Life-member of 5 National Horticultural Societies of India.

Dr. Parshant Bakshi is presently working as Associate Professor, Division of Fruit Science, Faculty of Agriculture, SKUAST-Jammu. He has handled 6 institutional and 9 externally projects. Guided 3 M.Sc. and 02 Ph.D students. He has published two books, one coffee table book and 65 articles in various national and international journals. He has been awarded as a Fellowship Award by Hi-tech Horticultural Society of India in 2012. He is a Life-member of 8 National Horticultural Societies of India. His web-portal www.krishisandesh.com, would give more detail related to various operational aspects and is the most cited web-portal for the last 4 years.

Olive: Response to Girdling, Micronutrients and Growth Retardants

Amit Jasrotia
V.K.Wali
Parshant Bakshi

2015
Scholars World
A Division of
Astral International Pvt. Ltd.
New Delhi – 110 002

Cataloging in Publication Data--DK

Courtesy: D.K. Agencies (P) Ltd. <docinfo@dkagencies.com>

Jasrotia, Amit, author.

Olive : response to girdling, micronutrients and growth retardants / Amit Jasrotia, V.K. Wali, Parshant Bakshi.

pages   cm

Includes bibliographical references (pages   ).
ISBN 9789351306207 (International)

1. Olive--India--Dharamthal. 2. Tree girdling--India--Dharamthal. 3. Trace elements--India--Dharamthal. 4. Dwarfism--India--Dharamthal.   I. Wali, V. K., author. II. Bakshi, Parshant, author. III. Title.

DDC 634.6309546   23

Published by   : **Scholars World**
                          A Division of
                          Astral International Pvt. Ltd.
                          – ISO 9001:2008 Certified Company –
                          4760-61/23, Ansari Road, Darya Ganj
                          New Delhi-110 002
                          Ph. 011-43549197, 23278134
                          E-mail: info@astralint.com
                          Website: www.astralint.com

Laser Typesetting   : **SSMG Computer Graphics**, Delhi - 110 084

Printed at   : **Thomson Press India Limited**

PRINTED IN INDIA

ACKNOWLEDGEMENTS

Pride, praise and perfection belong to almighty alone. So, first of all, I would like to thank 'HIM' for health and courage he bestowed on me to go through this project.

I express my loyal and heartiest thanks to my esteemed teacher and Chairman of my advisory committee Prof. V.K. Wali, Head, Division of Fruit Science for his expert, invaluable and tireless guidance, methodological approach of deep scientific vision for my professional growth. His humane treatment, meticulous planning and scrutiny of this draft inspite of enormous engagements are highly appreciated.

With profound sense of gratitude, I express my sincere thanks to worthy members of my advisory committe; Dr. Parshant Bakshi, Associate Professor, Dr. Mahital Jamwal, Asstt. Professor, Division of Fruit Science, Dr. A.K. Bhat, Professor, Division of Soil Science and Agricultural Chemistry, and Dr. R.K. Kaul, Professor and Head, Division of Food Science and Technology for their timely help and constructive criticism for finalization of this manuscript.

I sincerely acknowledge the help rendered by Dr. Manish Sharma, Associate Professor, Division of Agricultural Economics and Statistics for analysis of experimental data and Dr. Moni Gupta, Asstt. Professor, Division of Plant Physiology and Biochemistry for helping me in the biochemical analysis undertaken in my research programme.

With overwhelmimg sense of legitimate pride, I express my deep sentiments and gratitude to Prof. M.S. Bhadwal, Associate Dean, Faculty of Veterinary Science for constant encouragement and blessings.

I am also thankful to Sher-e-Kashmir University of Agricultural Sciences and Technology of Jammu for providing me an opportunity to go for higher studies as an in-service candidate.

I cannot eschew to express my whole hearted sense of reverence to my father Sh. K.S. Jasrotia and mother Smt. Raksha Jasrotia whose lively inspirations and blessings always proved to be strong feather against all odds.

My loving thanks and appreciations are also due to my wife Pooja and son Utkarsh for cheerfully sharing the difficulties during the period of study.

Help rendered by Sh. B.N. Singh, JTA, Division of Fruit Science is highly acknowledged. Last but not the least, I express my thanks to Mr. Hitesh Mittal, Vice President, Astral International (P) Ltd., New Delhi for publishing my manuscript in book form.

(Amit Jasrotia)

Jammu

CONTENTS

Acknowledgements   *v*

1   INTRODUCTION   1-3

2   REVIEW OF LITERATURE   4-36

3   MATERIALS AND METHODS   37-45

4   RESULTS   46-82

5   DISCUSSION   83-92

6   SUMMARY AND CONCLUSION   93-97

7   REFERENCES   98-118

CHAPTER 1
INTRODUCTION

Olive (*Olea europea* L.), commonly known as zaitoon, is one of the world's oldest cultivated crops, mention of which has been made in Holy Quran and Holy Bible. Olive is considered to be the native of Asia Minor, the areas lying between Armenia, Turkestan and Pamirs (Cimato and Bartolini, 1987). According to Vavilov (1951), the olive originated from an area corresponding to modern Syria and Iran whereas Almeida (1963) believe that olive originated in Afghanistan where there are numerous other species belonging to the family Oleaceae. The cultivation of olive started about 5000-6000 years ago and expanded from its origin to all around Mediterranean sea and the adjacent zones comprising Asia Minor, parts of India, Africa and Europe.

The olives are principally used for oil extraction all over the world, while some cultivars can also be used for pickling. Olive oil is used as cooking oil in all Mediterranean countries. It has got immense importance in human nutrition. Being rich source of polyunsaturated fatty acid and freedom of cholesterol makes it ideal oil as compared to many edible oils. Oil extracted from olive fruit is also used medicinally. It is a tonic, appetizer, useful in biliousness, scabies, thirst, burning of the eyes, caries of teeth, toothache. It is also purgative, useful in griping, pains in the joints, and rheumatism.

The area and production under olive in the world is 9.39 million ha and 20.58 million tonnes, respectively (FAO, 2012). The leading olive producing countries of the world are Spain, Italy, Greece, Portugal, Turkey, Syria, Jordan, etc. Spain is the leading producer of olive in the world.

In India, olive cultivation is extended in sub-mountainous region, encompassing the states of Jammu and Kashmir, Himachal Pradesh and hills of Uttar Pradesh lying between 30^0-35^0 N latitude. At present, India is importing considerable quantities of olive oil to meet its domestic requirement. So, in order to attain a state of self sufficiency in indigenous production of olive oil and to diversify horticulture industry, olive plantation has been raised in the northern hilly states of Jammu and Kashmir,

Himachal Pradesh and Uttranchal. The commercial olive cultivation in Jammu and Kashmir is only of recent origin which comprises an area of 480.69 ha with an annual production of 21.57 metric tonnes (Anonymous, 2011).

The present plantation has been raised in drought prone and rainfed areas situated in mid hills of Jammu and Kashmir comprising Doda, Ramban, Udhampur, Poonch, Rajouri, Baramulla and Kupwara districts. The growth flush of olive trees in these areas is confined to a very short period of 2-3 months. These areas experience mild and inadequate winter rains, which resulted in insufficient chilling of olive trees. Prevalence of such conditions not only restricts vegetative growth of olive trees but also inhibit the process of flower bud differentiation. One of the major concerns of olive growers in Jammu and Kashmir is that yields are often irregular and uneconomical. Poor fruit growth of such trees during autumn season results in poor flowering and consequently a poor fruit set and yield. Olive belongs to a group of fruit species with a distinct tendency towards alternate bearing under un-irrigated conditions. Alternate bearing is an overall response of cropping due to yearly overlapping between two successive biannual cycles. The total amount of shoot growth is greatly affected by the crop as fruit represents a major competitive sink (Rallo and Suarez, 1989). This behaviour is more striking in traditional and poorly managed orchards. The inconsistent and restricted uptake of nutrients, hormonal imbalances, improper pruning and lower soil fertility status are other factors, which also account for poor growth and yield of olive trees. Various cultural and environmental manipulations, such as pruning, drought, inadequate chilling, and light intensity, may influence flower bud formation and contribute to alternate bearing (Hartmann, 1953; Lavee, 1989).

In olive, fertilizer application programme mainly includes use of nitrogen, phosphorous and potassium and very little emphasis is laid on the use of micro-nutrients. However, during the last few decades, use of micro-nutrients in improving the qualitative and quantitative traits of fruit crops is well established. The foliar application of some micro-nutrients like boron and zinc help in increasing foliar zinc and boron level in the leaves, which improves fertilization and increase fruit set of olive trees (Talaie and Taheri, 2001; Maksoud *et al.*, 2004).

Boron is an essential nutrient for higher plants and its deficiency affects plant growth and yield in many parts of the world. A positive response to B application has been reported in over 80 countries and 132 crops during the last decades (Shorrocks, 1997). Olive is a sensitive crop to boron shortage. Deficiency affects not only the vegetative growth but also the reproductive processes through pre and post fertilization effects such as pollen development and germination, pistil development and number of perfect flowers, pollen tube growth, number of fertilized ovaries, fruitlet retention and growth (Shorrocks, 1997; Perica *et al.*, 2001). Boron sprays given three days prior to anthesis tended to increase its concentration in flowers and also increased fruit set (Delgado *et al.*, 1994). Similarly, zinc is another micro-nutrient whose role is indispensable in nutrition of olive trees. Role of zinc in improving the fruit set and fruit retention in olive has been well established by Taheri and Talaie (2001). They concluded that foliar application of zinc sulphate and boric acid at 0.5 %, one week before and at full bloom led to a considerable increase in fruit set and number of fruits retained in olive.

Endogenous levels of phytohormones are key factors controlling alternate bearing physiology in olives (Palese and Crocker, 2002). Plant growth retardants are commonly used in a great variety of fruit crops to modify the tree's vegetative growth and improve fruit setting and yield (Miller and Tworkoski, 2003; Rademacher, 2000). Paclobutrazol and cycocel have extensively been used to regulate cropping of fruit crops like mango, litchi, and olive. In these fruit crops, paclobutrazol has been reported to reduce shoot growth and increase bloom and yield (Porlingis *et* al., 1999; Asin *et al.*, 2007; Karuna and Mankar, 2008). Whereas, Hegazi and Stino (1982) reported that application of cycocel at 2000 ppm in olive cultivars increased the percentage of perfect flowers considerably.

The aim of girdling is accumulation of carbohydrates and hormones above the girdled portion by blocking the phloem continuum. These accumulated metabolites thus become available more to the metabolic sinks like differentiating flowers or developing fruits, which results in better flower and fruit retention. The effect of girdling on tree growth, fruit quality and yield is well documented in deciduous fruit crops (Noel, 1970; Grierson *et al.*, 1982; Goren *et al.*, 2004; Wargo *et al.*, 2004). In olive, girdling has also been reported to improve number of inflorescence, the number of perfect flowers, fruit set and yield (Lavee *et al.*, 1983; Ben-Tal and Lavee, 1984; Levin and Lavee, 2005).

On the basis of the research work carried out in olive on girdling (Lavee *et al.*, 1983; Ben-Tal and Lavee, 1984; Levin and Lavee, 2005), foliar feeding of micro-nutrients (Perica *et al.,* 2001; Taheri and Talaie 2001; Pedo *et al.*, 2005), and use of growth retardants (Hegazi and Stino, 1982; Antognozzi *et al.*, 1989; Proietti and Tombesi, 1996), the present studies were undertaken to regulate and improve the productivity of olive trees with the following objectives.

(i) To study the effect of girdling and foliar application of micro-nutrients on growth, yield and quality of olive cv. Frontoio.

(ii) To study the effect of growth retardants on growth, yield and quality of olive cv. Frontoio.

CHAPTER 2
REVIEW OF LITERATURE

In olives, the phenomenon of low productivity is mainly due to poor bloom, low percentage of perfect flowers or insufficient fruit set. The abscission of flower and fruit-let in olives is mostly responsible for the small percentage of fruits retained to maturity. It is very crucial to understand the various external and internal factors involved in flower induction in olive for achieving regularly higher yields. Horticultural techniques viz., girdling, pruning, use of growth retardants and micro-nutrients have been used to enhance the productivity in different fruit crops including olives. In this chapter, an attempt has been made to review the work done on the use of different horticultural techniques for improving the growth and productivity in different fruit crops including olives and are presented under the following headings.

I.   Studies on foliar application of micro-nutrients

II. Studies on girdling

III. Studies on use of growth retardants

2.1 STUDIES ON FOLIAR APPLICATION OF MICRO-NUTRIENTS

Foliar fertilizers are used both as a replacement for solids and their unique capacity to provide nutrients quickly and effectively. Foliar fertilization has been used by fruit growers since 19th century and has become an important management practice in well managed orchard systems particularly in dry farming system, where water is scarce. A significant commercial justification for the use of foliar fertilizers is based upon the premise that foliar fertilizers offer specific advantage over soil fertilizers under certain conditions of high nutrient demand e.g., during rapid fruit growth, when demand can exceed nutrient supply even in a fertile soil or occasions when localized within plant demand exceeds the capacity for within plant nutrient redistribution.

The foliar feeding of micro-nutrients in different fruit crops including olives has assumed a significant position to enhance their growth, productivity and nutrient status. As per the literature available on the effect of foliar feeding of micro-nutrients on the qualitative and quantitative characteristics, response to foliar application of zinc and boron in different fruit crops including olive is as under.

2.1.1 Zinc

2.1.1.1 Effect on growth

Singh and Rajput (1976) studied the effect of foliar sprays of $ZnSO_4$ at 0.2, 0.4, 0.6 and 0.8 per cent on vegetative growth in Chausa variety of mango and reported that zinc spray significantly improved the vegetative growth of mango in terms of shoot length, number of leaves and leaf area as compared to control. Similarly, in apple cvs. Kitaika and Grushovka Moskovskaya five applications of Zn or Cu each at 0.05% stimulated tree growth and increased root sugar and starch contents (Pirogova, 1979). Whereas Pelevina (1980) found that basal dressing of NPK in combination with foliar application of Zn (0.4%) on apple trees had a significant effect on the increase of leaf water retaining capacity as compared to control (NPK basal dressing alone).

In pecan, the growth and productivity improved considerably with foliar feeding of zinc as reported by Malstrom *et al.* (1984). They found that foliar applications of Zn were more effective than soil applications and provided adequate Zn for proper growth and productivity in pecans. Patel and Patel (1985) applied two/four foliar sprays of 0.5 or 1.0 per cent Zn and/or Fe between mid-November and May to acid lime (*Citrus aurantifolia* Swingle) trees. They estimated that the chlorophyll content was higher in trees receiving Zn at 0.5 per cent, than in trees receiving Fe at 1.0 per cent (2 sprays) or at 0.5 per cent (4 sprays), and highest in trees receiving Zn and Fe, each at 0.5 per cent.

The enhancement of vegetative growth with zinc sprays has also been reported in peach (Shishanku and Titova, 1992; Sandhu *et al.,* 1994) as well as in Royal Gala cultivar of apple by Pons (1996). Zinc application has been found to be useful in improving growth of Ber trees. It was observed by Singh and Ahlawat (1996) that application of 1.0 per cent $ZnSO_4$ resulted in maximum shoot extension growth and leaf area in treated trees. On the contrary, no growth response to foliar feeding of zinc has been obtained by Swietlik and LaDuke (1991) in 'Valencia' orange and 'Ruby Red' grapefruit and by Swietlik (1996) in 'Rio Red' grapefruit.

The synergistic effect of zinc and boron in promoting vegetative growth of young Fazli mango trees has been reported (Banik and Sen, 1997). The highest increase in plant height (61.0 cm) was observed with application of zinc 0.4 per cent and boron 0.1 per cent. They also found that boron 0.4 per cent and zinc 0.4 per cent resulted in maximum trunk girth. Lal *et al.* (1998) found that percentage increase in the stem girth of Dashehari mango trees was highest with the soil application of zinc sulphate at 0.5 kg/tree followed by foliar application of zinc sulphate at 1.0 per cent. The percent increase in the tree canopy volume was highest with the foliar application of zinc sulphate at 1.0 per cent followed by soil application of zinc sulphate at 1.0 kg/tree.

Walworth *et al.* (2006) reported that spring application of zinc sulphate @ 14 or 28 kg ha^{-1} increased leaf area in pecan trees as compared to fall application of same dose. Hamdy *et al.* (2007) studied the relation of fruiting in Hindy Bisinara mangoes to foliar nutrition with Mg, B and Zn and some antioxidants. They concluded that single or combined application of Tannic, Ascorbic and Citric acids each at 500 ppm as well as 0.5% Zn + 0.025% B + 0.25% Mg was favourable in improving the leaf area of mango.

Yadav *et al.* (2007) conducted an experiment to study the effect of zinc sulphate on the growth, yield and quality of sweet orange cv. Jaffa. Six levels of zinc sulphate as soil application (0, 50, 100, 150, 200 and 250 g per plant) and four levels of zinc sulphate as foliar spray (0, 0.25, 0.50 and 0.75 per cent) in combination with three spray schedule applied in 2nd week of May, last week of June and 2nd week of August. They found that plant height and spread was maximum with soil application of 250 g zinc sulphate per plant. However, foliar application of 0.75 percent zinc sulphate gave best results in term of plant growth.

In a study, on the effect of micro-nutrients on growth and yield of mango cv. Dashehari conducted by Singh *et al.* (2009), it was found that interactions of zinc and manganese at higher levels and boron either at lower or higher concentration caused significant improvement in vegetative growth of mango cv. Dashehari in relation to length and girth of the shoots and number of leaves per shoot. Out of three micronutrients *viz.*, zinc, manganese and boron, zinc produced maximum length and width of panicles followed by boron and manganese. Rajaie *et al.* (2009) while studying the effect of zinc and boron interaction on growth and mineral composition of lemon seedlings (*Citrus aurantifolia* L) in a calcareous soil observed that application of 10 and 2.5 µg g^{-1} soil zinc and boron, respectively resulted into best plant production and the combination was associated with the highest uptake of N, P, K, Zn, Fe, Cu and Mn under greenhouse conditions.

An experiment was conducted by Keshavarz *et al.* (2011) to evaluate the effect of zinc (0, 1050 and 1750 mg L^{-1}) and boron (0, 174 and 348 mg L^{-1}) applied singly or in combination in Persian walnut (*Juglans regia*). They found that the chlorophyll index was highest at 1050 and 174 mg L^{-1} Zn and boron, respectively and the same combination resulted in the longest new shoot growth. They also reported that the highest concentration of N in leaves was achieved with application of 174 mg L^{-1} boron in combination with 1750 mg L^{-1} zinc.

2.1.1.2 Effect on flowering and fruit set

Zinc is required to obtain good fruit set and size. Its role in flowering is due to the synthesis of tryptophan which is a precursor of auxin and promotes flowering. It also helps in the process of translocation of metabolites to the bud itself or to the site of bud development. The application of zinc in the form of zinc sulphate has been reported to show a marked improvement in flowering and fruit set of fruit trees. An investigation on the effect of zinc sprays on flowering of mango cv. Chausa revealed that application of ZnSO$_4$ (0.8 per cent) increased the length of panicle and number of hermaphrodite flowers (Singh and Rajput, 1976). However, Daulta *et al.* (1981) reported that zinc had no appreciable effect on number of hermaphrodite flowers but increased fruit set of mango cv. Dashehari. Mansour and El-Sied (1981) obtained increase in fruit set and reduction of pre-harvest fruit drop in guava following spray of $ZnSO_4$ (0.5 and 1.0 per cent) at full bloom.

Results of several research works indicate that Zn plays an important role in pollination and fertilization of flowers and as a result increased fruit set has been observed in orange by Qin (1996) with foliar application of zinc. Arora and Yamdagni (1986) studied the effect of different doses of nitrogen and zinc sprays on flowering, fruit set and final fruit retention in sweet lime (*C. limettioides* Tanaka.). They found that 1000 g N/tree and two sprays of Zn (0.5 per cent), increased the number of flowers/shoot, the percentage of hermaphrodite flowers, fruit set and final fruit retention in sweet lime.

Singh and Rethy (1996) studied the effect of zinc, copper, boron and NAA on the yield of 16-year-old kagzi lime. The highest number of flowers per twig was recorded with the application of $ZnSO_4$ (0.5 per cent) in combination with NAA (20 ppm). Banik *et al.* (1999) studied the effect of foliar application of Zn, Fe and B in combination with urea on flowering and fruit set in mango cultivar Fazli. They found that all the micronutrients significantly influenced the proportion of flowering shoots, panicle size, number of hermaphrodite flowers and consequently resulted in enhanced fruit set.

Stover *et al.* (1999) while studying the effect of pre-bloom foliar application of boron, zinc, and urea on cropping of 'Empire' and 'McIntosh' apple orchards found that pre-bloom nutrients did not enhance spur leaf development or fruit set; such treatments probably enhanced cropping by increasing retention of flower buds that would otherwise abscise before anthesis. Sotomayor *et al.* (2000) reported that the final fruit set in Non-Pariel variety of almond increased by 27.7 and 23.4 per cent with foliar spray of boric acid (0.2%) and zinc (0.4%) applied singly, respectively. A combined application of zinc and boron caused 38.1 per cent increase in the final fruit set and a 15 per cent increase in almond yields.

In olives, Taheri and Talaie (2001) concluded that foliar application of zinc sulphate and boric acid at 0.5% one week before and at full bloom led to a considerable increase in fruit set and fruit retention. In another report by Talaie and Taheri (2001) boron and zinc sprays caused a significant increase in final fruit set of olives by decreasing the formation of shot berries and consequently the abscission of young fruits.

Ebeed *et* al. (2001) recorded significantly higher fruit number per panicle compared to the control with combined sprays of zinc, manganese and iron in mango cv. Mesk. They also found a beneficial effect of combined sprays of zinc, manganese and iron in reducing fruit drop percentage. In Purbi cultivar of litchi, Borun and Kumar (2003) obtained maximum fruit set with the application of $ZnSO_4$ (0.5%), whereas in almond Bybordi and Malakouti (2006) studied the effect of foliar application of urea (0 and 500 mg N/Kg), zinc sulphate (0, 2500, 5000 mg Zn/Kg), and boric acid (0, 1000, 2000 mg B/Kg) on per cent fruit set and observed that the highest rate of initial fruit set of 24 per cent was obtained with boron treatment at 2000 mg /Kg followed by 22 per cent with zinc at 5000 mg /Kg.

An experiment was conducted by Yadav *et al.* (2007), to study the effect of zinc sulphate on the growth, yield and quality of sweet orange cv. Jaffa wherein they found that both soil and foliar application influenced growth as well as fruit drop in Jaffa sweet orange and application of zinc sulphate (0.75%) thrice i.e., in second week of May, last week of June and second week of August resulted in better growth and less fruit drop. In Washington Navel, another cultivar of Sweet Orange, Eman *et al.* (2007) used GA_3 and zinc sprays for improving yield and fruit quality. They found that spraying chelated zinc (0.4%) alone or with GA_3 (20 ppm) significantly increased fruit set, fruit retention and decreased fruit drop.

Syamal *et al.* (2008) studied the effect of foliar spray of urea (0, 2 and 4%) and zinc sulphate (0, 0.2 and 0.4%) on the growth, flowering, fruiting and fruit quality of 10-year-old trees of kagzi lime. The minimum duration of flowering and maximum number of flowers were recorded in trees which received urea (4%) and zinc sulphate (0.4%). The minimum fruit drop and maximum fruit retention was recorded in trees sprayed with urea (4%) and zinc sulphate (0.4%), respectively.

Kumar *et al.* (2008) investigated the effect of foliar application of mineral nutrients on flowering and fruiting character of Amrapali mango wherein urea, zinc sulphate and borax were sprayed at different levels alone or in combination and observed remarkable influence of different nutrients on flowering and fruiting characters. However, foliar application of urea (2%) in combination with $ZnSO_4$ (0.5%) or borax (0.5%) were the most effective treatments in improving the flowering and fruiting characters. Ramezani *et al.* (2010) sprayed 'Shengeh' olive trees with GA_3 (0, 15, 30, and 45 ppm) and $ZnSO_4$ (0, 0.25, 0.50, and 0.75%) in August (about halfway through the fruit growth period) and obtained maximum fruit retention (90%) with spray of $ZnSO_4$ (0.5%) and GA_3 (45 ppm).

2.1.1.3 Effect on fruit quality and yield

In olives, according to Jordao and Lietao (1990) fruit weight, oil content, and percentage of shotberry fruits depended on mineral status of leave and fruit tissues, and thus by the nutrient management of the orchard for maintaining the optimum levels of minerals concentrations of nitrogen, boron and zinc in leaves and fruits, improvement of fruit quality and yield of olive oils can be achieved.

Singh and Rajput (1976) reported that with increasing concentration of $ZnSO_4$, there was an increase in fruit weight of mango cv. Chausa. The maximum fruit weight was attained with spray of $ZnSO_4$ (0.8%). Whereas in cashewnut, $ZnSO_4$ or urea, both at 1.0, 2.5 or 4.0% concentration, or NAA at 50 and 100 ppm were applied to 11 to 13-year-old trees in the second week of April. The nuts were harvested 25 days later. The highest nut yield (5.85 kg/tree) was obtained with $ZnSO_4$ (4.0%) as compared to 4.29 kg/tree in control trees (Bera *et al.*, 1988). A positive correlation between the fruit Zn concentration and the weight and oil content of the olive fruit has been observed by Jordao and Lietao (1990).

In kagzi lime, maximum number of flowers per twig and highest yield of fruits in kg/plant was recorded by Singh and Rethy (1996) with $ZnSO_4$ (0.5%) in combination with NAA (20 ppm). Maximum average fresh individual fruit weight was recorded with zinc (0.5 or 1%) in combination with NAA 20 ppm. A significant increase in fruit weight after zinc and boron application has also been reported in mango (Rath *et al.*, 1980; Banik and Sen, 1997). Banik *et al.* (1999) while studying the effect of zinc, iron and boron in combination with urea on growth, flowering, fruiting and fruit quality of mango cv Fazli, found that all the micro-nutrients significantly influenced the fruiting and fruit quality particularly at higher concentrations. However, combined application of zinc (0.4%) and urea (1%) resulted in highest fruit number (48) and yield (32.53 kg/plant) as compared with 32 and 20.38 kg/plant, respectively in control.

In another study on the effect of soil and foliar application of zinc and copper on yield and fruit quality of seedless lemon, Sharma *et al.* (1999) reported highest yield of fruits with foliar sprays of Zn-EDTA (0.4%) in combination with Cu-EDTA (0.2%). In a study conducted by El-Saida (2001) in Egypt to investigate the effects of 0.5% $ZnSO_4$ applied three times and two types of growth substances (GA_3 15 ppm and Biozem 1.5 ml/l) as foliar sprays at 30 and 70 per cent flowering of sweet orange cv. Washington Navel found that $ZnSO_4$ in combination with Biozem or GA_3, significantly increased final yield through increased fruit set, efficiency of fruiting and decreased June-drop and pre-harvest drop. $ZnSO_4$ incombination with Biozem improved leaf dry matter and leaf contents of Ca, Fe, Zn and Mn, but had no effect on the leaf N, P and K contents. The same treatment also improved the physical characteristics of fruits.

In olives, Taheri and Talaie (2001) reported that foliar application of Zn (0.5%), one week before full bloom, improved Zn status of leaves and fruit flesh which was positively correlated with oil content of fruits. Boron and zinc sulphate had significant effect on the concentration of N, P and K in leaves and fruits. Ebeed *et al.* (2001) reported that spraying the mango trees with a combination of Fe, Zn and Mn increased tree yield, fruit weight, pulp weight, and pulp/fruit weight.

Application of zinc sulphate (0.5%) alone or in combination with 2,4,5-T (20ppm) and GA_3 (50 ppm) on Kagzi lime plants, significantly increased fruit weight and volume (Sharma *et al.*, 2003). Wali *et al.* (2005) observed that yield of phalsa (*Grewia subinaequalis* DC) cv. Purple Round, increased significantly with foliar application of urea, potassium and zinc. The highest yield was recorded with zinc sulphate (0.6%). Both $ZnSO_4$ (0.6%) and combined sprays of urea and potassium sulphate improved yield and physico-chemical composition of phalsa. In almonds, Bybordi and Malakouti (2006) recorded highest per cent oil content in the kernels with zinc application.

A study was conducted to determine the effects of magnesium, zinc and manganese on enhancing the productivity and quality of Kinnow mandarin by Babu *et al.* (2007) who found that spray of magnesium sulphate (0.5%), zinc sulphate (0.5%) and/or manganese sulphate (0.5%) fruit number was maximum in trees sprayed with zinc and manganese, and minimum in the control trees whereas fruit weight, fruit volume and fruit length was maximum in trees sprayed with magnesium, zinc and manganese, and minimum in the control. They also observed that spraying essential elements either singly or in combination was effective in obtaining a higher productivity. The highest productivity of 34.07 kg/tree was recorded with zinc and manganese spray. Omaima and El-Metwally (2007) also observed that application of Zn (0.5%) and K (1.0%) alone or in combination significantly improved physical and chemical characteristics of fruit and yield (kg/tree) in Washington Navel orange. They also found that application of Zn and K alone or in combination significantly increased leaf N, P, K and Zn content.

Hamdy *et al.* (2007) studied relation of fruiting in Hindy Bisinara mangoes to foliar nutrition with Mg, B and Zn and some antioxidants. They showed that single or combined application of Tannic, Ascorbic and Citric acids and Zn+B+Mg improved yield and quality parameters. The best results with regard to yield and fruit quality were obtained with citric acid (500 ppm) + chelated Zn (0.05%) + boric acid (0.025%) + magnesium sulphate (0.25%) applied four times. Foliar application of Zn, B and Mg also improved N, P, K, Mg, Zn and Fe contents in mango leaves. Kangarshahi *et al.* (2007) found that foliar application of zinc (4 kg $ZnSO_4$ in 1000 litre of water) on Satsuma mandarins resulted in highest yield, average fruit weight and fruit diameter.

Eman *et al.* (2007) observed that spraying chelated zinc (0.4%) alone or with GA_3 (20 ppm) significantly increased fruit set, fruit retention, decreased fruit drop and subsequently improved the yield as well as the physical fruit characteristics of Washington Navel orange. Zinc sprays also improved leaf N, K and Zn contents. Tariq *et al.* (2007) obtained maximum fruit size and fruit volume with foliar spray of Zn and B and with Zn and Mn, respectively. Therefore, they suggested that either Zn and Mn or Zn and B may be applied as foliar spray in combination with urea and surfactant for getting the maximum yield and improved quality of Blood Red cultivar of sweet orange.

The effectiveness of soil and foliar fertilizer applications of nitrogen and zinc on growth, yield, and quality of apple (*Malus domestica* Borkh) cv. Golden Delicious was studied by Amiri *et al.* (2008) who recorded the highest yield (49 kg tree^{-1}), and the heaviest fruits (202 g) with the soil fertilization (276 g N tree^{-1} year^{-1} and 110 g Zn tree^{-1} year^{-1}) and foliar spray (N 10 g urea L^{-1} and Zn 8 g $ZnSO_4$ L^{-1}) treatment combination. Kumar *et al.* (2008) reported that foliar application of urea (2%) along with $ZnSO_4$ either 0.5% or 1.0% was most effective treatment in improving yield of mango cv. Amrapali. In the same cultivar of mango Vejendla *et al.* (2008) observed that spray of $ZnSO_4$ (0.75%) resulted into significantly higher fruit weight (216.83 g), pulp (71.90 per cent), lower peel and stone percentage.

Singh *et al.* (2009) also reported that different concentrations of zinc sulphate, manganese sulphate, boric acid and their combinations significantly increased fruit size in the form of fruit length and width in mango. Rajaie *et al.* (2009) observed that application of B and Zn (2.5 and 10 micro g g^{-1} soil) in combination, was associated with the highest uptake of Zn, N, P, K, Fe, Mn and Cu in lemon plants under greenhouse conditions and they suggested that the combination resulted into a suitable condition in which plants had a well-balanced nutritional status.

A study was conducted on ten-year-old 'Shengeh' olive trees by Ramezani *et al.* (2010) to investigate the effect of GA_3 and $ZnSO_4$ sprays on fruit yield and oil production. They observed highest fruit weight (3.25 g/fruit) with GA_3 (30 ppm) and $ZnSO_4$ (0.75%). The highest oil per cent on a dry weight basis (34.75%) was recorded with $ZnSO_4$ (0.50%) and GA_3 (30 ppm). Gonzalez *et al.* (2010) reported that zinc applied to the foliage of 'Washington' navel orange trees at 10% anthesis significantly increased fruit retention and consequently the fruit yield compared to untreated control.

Khafagy *et al*. (2010) showed that single or combined application of either yeast extract or zinc on Navel orange trees was very effective in stimulating yield as well as fruit weight, length and volume. Muhammad *et al*. (2010) reported that foliar application of Zn and B in sweet orange significantly influenced the days to flowering, fruit yield tree[-1],whereas per cent fruit set and per cent fruit drop were not significantly affected by foliar spray of Zn and B alone or either in combination.

In mango cv. Himsagar, Bhowmick and Banik (2011) observed that with the increase in concentration of spray solution of $ZnSO_4$ from 0.5 to 1.0% there was an increase in fruit retention, yield and fruit size but fruit retention, yield and size decreased as concentration of spray solution was increased to 1.5% $ZnSO_4$. Pandit *et al*. (2011) studied the effect of foliar application of boron and zinc on fruit set and productivity of almond and observed that combined application of boric acid 2000 ppm and zinc sulphate 4000 ppm resulted in significant increase in final fruit set and consequently fruit yield. Kehavarz *et al*. (2011) reported that foliar application of boron (174 mg L[-1]) in combination with zinc (1050 mg L[-1]) increased walnut yield by 400% as compared to untreated trees.

2.1.2 Boron

2.1.2.1 Effect on growth

Foliar application of boric acid (0.05 %) at the green bud stage resulted in a higher growth and leaf area of apple trees (Ljubkin, 1969). However, Jovanovic (1972) reported that both foliar and soil applications of boron increased leaf chlorophyll content in Golden Delicious apple. Potopova (1974) also reported an increase in leaf area and leaf dry weight in apple trees sprayed with H_3BO_3. Similarly, Singh and Singh (1976) observed that boron (0.2 or 0.4%), especially at the higher rate, increased shoot growth and total leaf area of kagzi lime (*Citrus aurantifolia* Swingle).

Rajput *et al*. (1976) applied boric acid (0, 0.2, 0.4, 0.6 or 0.8%) in Langra mango trees, just before flowering and obtained proportionate increase in growth characteristics viz., length of terminal shoot and number of leaves per shoot, with the increase in concentration of boric acid up to 0.8 per cent. Similarly, Singh (1977) sprayed Langra mango trees with boric acid (0.2, 0.4, 0.6 or 0.8%) and observed that leaf numbers and dry weight was significantly increased by all the treatments. However, use of excessive concentrations of boron has been reported to show a depressing effect on shoot growth of young apple trees (Hansen, 1981).

Kilany and Kilany (1991) used boric acid (0.086 to 0.172 %) as foliar sprays and observed that application of boric acid at varying concentrations registered a significant increase in shoot length and diameter in Anna cultivar of apple. Wojcik and Mika (1996) also observed that foliar application of B thrice, either before or after flowering increased tree growth in apple.

Foliar application of Zn (0.1, 0.2 and 0.4%, as zinc sulphate), Fe (0.1, 0.2 and 0.4%, as ferrous sulphate) and B (0.1, 0.2 and 0.4%, as borax) was made to 6-year-old plants of mango cv. Fazli in July and October by Banik and Sen (1997). They reported that both Zn and B promoted vegetative growth as indicated by plant height, trunk girth and spread of the young plants. The effect of Fe was less pronounced than those of B and Zn. Wojcik (1998) reported that boron application in plum also increased the number of shoots but had no effects on trunk cross sectional area.

Dutta (2004) reported that foliar application of boric acid (0, 500, 1000, 2000, 3000 and 4000 ppm) at bud swelling stage resulted in the promotion of vegetative growth in Himsagar mango and recorded maximum increase in the length of panicle with boric acid (3000 ppm) followed by boric acid 4000 ppm, while minimum was recorded in control. The diameter of rachis was minimum in control and maximum in 3000 ppm boric acid. Jiang *et al.* (2009) while working with Newhall Navel orange (*Citrus sinensis* Osbeck Newhall) trees supplied with B (0 and 15 g/plant) observed that boron application improved the growth of the navel orange trees and their boron nourishment condition as compared with untreated trees.

2.1.2.2   Effect on flowering and fruit set

Boron plays a very important role in pollen germination and pollen tube growth thus overcoming the problem of flower abortion which leads to increased fruit set (Griggs and Iwakiri, 1975; Lovatt, 1991). Application of boric acid @ 0, 0.2, 0.4, 0.6 or 0.8% in Langra mango trees, just before flowering resulted in an increase in number of fruits per panicle. There was a corresponding decline in per cent fruit drop with increasing concentration of boric acid (Rajput *et al.*, 1976).

Delgado *et al.* (1994) reported that the application of boron to olive trees at the time of anthesis increased boron content in leaf blades, petioles, bark of the flowering shoots and flowers. They further suggested that B is mobilized from young leaves during anthesis to fulfill the requirement of flowers and young fruits.

Haggag *et al.* (1995) observed that foliar application of boric acid at (500-1250 ppm) at late bud-swelling stage significantly increased the percentage of hermaphrodite flowers in mango (*Mangifera indica* L.) cv. Hindy Bisinnara. Favourable influence of boron on fruit set in apple has been reported by Gu *et al.* (1995), who observed that apple trees sprayed with B had a fruit set of 46.9-69.2% compared with 40.8-50.8% in control. They further stated that foliar application of boron also increased the chlorophyll content of the leaves.

Nyomora *et al.* (1997) studied the effect of foliar application of B in autumn on fruit set and tissue B concentration in open-pollinated Butte and Mono almond trees. The highest initial and second fruit set were associated with B application at 245 ppm or 490 ppm in both cultivars. This increased fruit set resulted in yield increase of 53% and 4%, respectively, for Butte and Mono.

Zude *et al.* (1998) concluded that application of boron to Elstar apple trees in autumn increased fruit set, however, no such effects were observed in trees sprayed in spring. Foliar application of boric acid at different concentrations improved fruit set, tissue boron concentration and fruit quality in almond (Nyomora *et al.*, 1999) and litchi (Dutta *et al.*, 2000). Sotomayor *et al.* (2000) also reported that a combined application of zinc and boron resulted in an increase of 38.1 per cent in the final fruit set of almond whereas with boron and zinc applied singly, the increase in fruit set was 27.7 and 22.2%, respectively as compared to control.

In olives, Perica *et al.* (2001) also obtained enhancement in fruit set by 43% to 54% in response to B applications at different concentrations over control. They also observed that increase in fruit set was not accompanied by decrease in fruit size. Nevertheless, beneficial effects of foliar B application varied between years and were greater when fruit set was low. Brown (2001) also reported that foliar B application immediately after pre-anthesis significantly altered the ratio of perfect to imperfect flower and increased fruit set in olive cv. Manzanillo.

Boron was applied to olive cv. Manzanillo trees at 0, 246, 491 and 737 mg L^{-1} and the percentage of perfect flowers was lowest in the control, which increased significantly with the increasing boron concentrations up to 491 mg L^{-1}, with a maximum increase of 49%. However, a further increase to 737 mg L^{-1} did not increase the response (Perica *et al.*, 2002).

Dutta (2004) reported that spray of boric acid (3000 ppm) at the late bud swell stage resulted in highest percentage of hermaphrodite flowers and fruit retention in mango cv. Himsagar. In a study conducted by Huang *et al.* (2005) in chestnut cultivars Maobanhong and Kuili, borax applied to the soil (15 g/m^2 soil) significantly reduced the abortion rate to 4.38% and 3.45%, respectively, compared with 42.2% and 50.6% in the controls. They further observed that borax (0.3%) twice at the flowering stage also greatly reduced the abortion rate with an increase of 46.8-52.9% in yield. In olive, Pedo *et al.* (2005) reported that pre- and post-anthesis application of B increased leaf B concentration and fruit set.

In almond cultivars Desmayo Largueta and Marcona, boron (832 ppm) was applied as single spray in early spring (two months after full bloom) or two weeks after fruit harvest or two sprays of B, one in early spring and other after fruit harvest. Two foliar B sprays significantly increased per cent fruit set as compared to single spray and control (Rufat and Arbones, 2006).

Kumar *et al.* (2008) found that foliar application of urea 2% in combination with $ZnSO_4$ 0.5% or borax 0.5% was the most effective treatment for improving the flowering and fruiting characters of Amrapali mango. Jiang *et al.* (2009) observed that in Newhall Navel orange (*Citrus sinensis* Osbeck Newhall) trees supplied with B (15 g/plant), the number of fruits per plant increased by 39.8%, fruit weight by 11.9% and fruit yield/ha by 23.3%, compared with control.

Foliar boron application significantly increased the fruit set in both "on" and "off" cropped trees of olive. In the first year of the experiment (off crop year), B sprays increased the fruit set more than soil application. Response to boron applications varied between years and were greater when fruit set was low. Application of boron (0.4%) was the most economic and effective dose for increasing fruit yield in olives (Soyergin, 2010). However, Stellacci *et al.* (2010) reported that neither fruit set nor yield were influenced by foliar application of B in olive.

Zinc sulphate in combination with boric acid significantly increased percentage of hermaphrodite flowers in mango cv. Dashehari (Negi *et al.*, 2010). In Amrpalli mango, Rajak *et al.* (2010) applied two sprays of borax (0.2, 0.4, 0.6, 0.8 and 1%), first given before panicle initiation and second just after fruit set, and observed that the date of panicle emergence was recorded first and initial number of fruit setting was found in favour of borax (1%) whereas, borax 1% and 0.8% spray proved to be the best treatment in reducing fruit drop percentage. Better fruit retention in response to boron has also been obtained in aonla by Yadav *et al.* (2010).

Pandit *et al.* (2011) studied the effect of boron (1000 and 2000 ppm) and zinc (2000 and 4000 ppm) on fruit set of almond cv. Shalimar. They observed that boron application increased fruit set from 8.4 per cent in control to 14.1 per cent with 2000 ppm boron. However, highest fruit set was recorded with combined application of boron and zinc, 2000 ppm and 4000 ppm, respectively.

Ahmad *et al.* (2011) sprayed Uslu cultivar of olive plants with B (0, 0.3, 0.6 and 0.9%) and GA_3 (0, 20 ppm, 25 ppm and 30 ppm) after flower opening. They obtained maximum number of flowers (2557) with the application of B (0.3%), while with GA_3 maximum number of flowers were obtained with 30 ppm (2222). Maximum fruit setting of 34 percent was recorded with B (0.6%) spray as compared to 21 percent observed with GA_3 (20 ppm). Thus, they concluded that B (0.9%) and GA_3 (30 ppm) was optimum for improvement in number of flowers and fruits.

2.1.2.3 Effect on fruit quality and yield

The enhancement of yield by foliar B application in perennial tree crops has long been recognized. Boron application increases fruit set and yield in several fruit and nut crops, (Jovanovic, 1972; Chaplin *et al.*, 1977; Hanson, 1991; Nyomara *et al.*, 1997).

Foliar B and Mn application in 10-year-old Golden Delicious trees increased the leaf N, P, K, Mg, Mn and B contents and reduced the Fe content. Soil applications did not affect leaf nutrient content. Both foliar and soil applications increased leaf chlorophyll content and thickness (Jovanovic, 1972). Almost similar observations have been made by Dixon *et al.* (1973) who reported an increase in B, Ca and K content as a result of B sprays.

Rajput *et al.* (1976) found an increase in fruit weight and fruit length with foliar application of boron (0.2, 0.4, 0.6 or 0.8%) in mango cv. Langra over control. Length of fruit was significantly more in only 0.6 and 0.8% boric acid spray, but increase of fruit width was recorded only up to 0.4% B spray. Singh (1977) sprayed mango trees of cv. Langra with boric acid (0.2, 0.4, 0.6 or 0.8%) and observed that leaf N content was increased with boron (0.2%) as compared to control, but was reduced at higher concentrations of boron. Rath *et al.* (1980) sprayed 13-year-old trees of the mango cv. Langra with B or Zn, each at 0.2-0.8%, at full bloom and found that fruit length, diameter and weight increased appreciably with B or Zn application.

Five-year-old trees of apple cv. Anna were treated with K_2SO_4, as a soil application (450 or 900 g/tree) or as a foliar spray (0.75 or 1.5%), and with H_3BO_3 as a soil application (75 or 150 g/tree) or as a foliar spray (0.086 or 0.172%). Both soil and foliar applications of H_3BO_3 significantly increased the yield. The highest fruit weight and fruit size was obtained with 1.5% K_2SO_4 and 0.172% H_3BO_3 foliar sprays (Kilany and Kilany, 1991). Foliar spray of boron (3 g/litre) on 5-year-old Tommy Atkins mango trees, applied once when the flower panicles began to appear, or when they began to open, or at both stages resulted in higher yields (22 kg/tree), as compared to 14 kg/tree for control (Coetzer *et al.*, 1991).

Singh and Khan (1993) applied Cu, Zn and B as foliar spray on 28-year-old mango cv. Dashehari trees in September/October, when fruits were at the pea stage. Yield (kg fruits/tree) decreased with increasing concentration of trace elements, however, individual fruit weight increased and fruit number decreased. Svagzdys (1995) found that application of boric acid (0.05 or 0.1%) for two successive years on apple cv. Cortland trees at or after flowering increased the yield by 21.1-22.7% in the second year and yield increase was maintained in the following year, especially with the sprays done after flowering.

Qin (1996) reported that H_3BO_3 (0.2%), $ZnSO_4$ (0.1%) or $MgSO_4$ (0.2%) sprayed at pre-anthesis, full bloom and young fruit development on Jincheng orange (*Citrus sinensis*) trees resulted into pollen tube elongation of 17.26, 7.85 and 23.97% respectively, than control, thus favouring fertilization and improving fruit set. He also found that foliar application of boron increased fruit yield and fruit size.

An experiment was conducted by Banik *et al.* (1997) to study the effect of foliar application of zinc, iron and boron, each at 0.1, 0.2 or 0.4%, on 30-year-old mango cv. Fazli trees and observed that Zn (0.4%) in combination with Fe and B (0.1%) produced maximum number of fruits/tree (621) and the highest yield of 462.1 kg/tree as compared to 356 number of fruits per tree and 230 kg/tree in control. They also obtained maximum fruit weight (839.3 g) and length (16.76 cm) with foliar sprays of B (0.4%) combined with Zn and Fe (0.2%). However, Castro and Sotomayor (1998) found that foliar application of Zn (750 and 1500 ppm) and B (170 and 340 ppm) alone or in combination to almond cultivars Non Pareil, Price, Solano and Carmel when flower buds were 10% open did not increase fruit set and had no effect on either fruit or seed weight or seed length. They also observed that two natural periods of fruit drop at 15 and 40 days after full bloom were not affected by the treatments.

Nyomora *et al.* (1999) reported that when boron (0, 0.8 or 1.7 kg/ha) was applied to almond cv. Butte, in September (three weeks postharvest), December (dormancy) or February (budbreak). September application effectively increased tissue B concentration, fruit set and yield than December or February applications. At another location, boron (0, 0.8, 1.25, 1.7 or 2.1 kg/ha) sprayed in almond trees during August, September or February. Boron at the highest rate (2.1 kg/ha) in September produced the greatest final fruit set and yield. February applications increased initial fruit set at both sites but were less effective than September applications at increasing yield. These results suggested that B should be applied immediately after harvest (September) for optimal effect on tissue B concentration, fruit set and yield in almond. Boron sprays after flowering increased fruit set and apple yield, however, decreased mean fruit weight (Wojcik, *et al.*, 1999).

Boron was applied to olive cv. Manzanillo trees at 0, 246, 491 and 737 mg L^{-1}. The application of 246 mg L^{-1} B increased yield by 30%. However, higher B concentrations (491 and 737 mg L^{-1}) increased yield only by 6% and 1%, over control. Foliar application of B increased fruit set and this increase in fruit set did not accompany the reduction in fruit size, thus enhancing yield and quality (Perica *et al.*, 2001). Similarly, Brown (2001) obtained increased fruit yield of olive, in response to foliar application of B done three weeks before anthesis.

Dutta (2004) applied boric acid (0, 500, 1000, 2000, 3000 and 4000 ppm) as foliar spray to Himsagar mango trees and obtained highest fruit length, breadth and weight, and pulp weight with boric acid (3000 ppm). Maksoud *et al.* (2004) reported that application of boron (500 ppm) along with urea (0.2 %) before or after full bloom increased leaf boron content in olive cv. Chemlali.

In almond, Rufat and Arbones (2006) applied boron (832 ppm) as single spray in early spring (two months after full bloom) or a single spray two weeks after fruit harvest and two sprays of boron (one in early spring and other after fruit harvest) and observed that the number of fruits increased and average fruit weight decreased in response to foliar sprays. Further they found that cumulative kernel yields were higher for the trees which were sprayed twice with B compared to untreated and spring treated trees. Similarly, Bybordi and Malakouti (2006) also reported that boron application at the highest rate improved the quantitative parameters such as weight, length and width of single almond fruit.

The effect of foliar as well as soil application of Ca and B on yield and quality of Red Delicious apple trees was studied by Lone (2007). He observed that apple trees receiving boron (0.1%) as foliar spray and calcium chloride (100 g/tree) in soil, gave better yields and fruit quality. Khalifa *et al.* (2009) studied influence of foliar spray of boron and calcium on productivity, fruit quality, and nutritional status of Anna apple trees. They observed that foliar application of boric acid and calcium chloride alone or in combinations significantly increased fruit yield and improved fruit physical and chemical properties as well as enhanced the nutritional status of apple trees.

Rajaie *et al.* (2009) evaluated the impact of different concentration of zinc and boron on growth and mineral composition of lemon seedlings (*Citrus aurantifolia* L.). They found that application of B and Zn (2.5 and 10 micro g g^{-1} soil) was associated with the highest uptake of Zn, N, P, K which resulted into a suitable condition in which plants had a well-balanced nutritional status.

In an experiment on olives conducted by Desouky *et al.* (2009), boron (0, 50 and 100 ppm) and calcium (0, 1 and 2%) sprayed twice (at full bloom and 15 days later) alone or in different combinations showed that spraying olive trees with boron (100 ppm) along with calcium (2%) proved to be best for good fruit set, oil content and oil quality. However, Stellacci *et al.* (2010) observed that in olive cultivar Leccino, neither fruit set nor yield was influenced by foliar application of boron.

Soyergin (2010) reported that foliar application of boron twice; before flowering and after fruit set, significantly increased leaf boron, yield and quality of olive cv. Manzanillo. Boron has been reported to improve fruit weight, volume and pulp: stone ratio in aonla (Yadav *et al.*, 2010). Rajak *et al.* (2010) found that two sprays of borax (1%) increased fruit weight and volume in Amrapali mango.

Pandit *et al.* (2011) reported that combined application of B and Zn at 2000 ppm and 4000 ppm, respectively resulted in highest fruit yield (3.65 Kg tree^{-1}) which was 32.7 per cent higher as compared to control (2.75 Kg tree^{-1}) in almond cultivar Shalimar.

Ahmad *et al.* (2011) reported that plants of olive cv. Uslu when sprayed with boron (0, 0.3, 0.06 and 0.09%) and GA_3 (0, 20, 25 and 30 ppm) after flower opening gave maximum number of fruits, fruit size and fruit weight with 30 ppm GA_3 (25 no., 3.79 cm and 3.65 g, respectively) and maximum number of fruits, fruit size and fruit weight with boron 0.09% (63.50 no., 1.712 cm and 3.562 g, respectively). Bhowmick and Banik (2011) reported that in mango cv. Himsagar increasing concentration of borax spray from 0.25% to 0.50% increased yield, fruit size and weight. However, a further increase in concentration of borax spray to 0.75% decreased yield, fruit size and weight.

2.2 STUDIES ON GIRDLING

Girdling is one of the many options to control excessive shoot growth and to accelerate fruit maturation. Girdling temporarily diverts photosynthates to the shoots above the girdled portion, resulting in the decline in root growth. The absorption of inorganic elements and the production of growth regulators such as cytokinins are thus reduced in the root. As a result vegetative growth of the tree is decreased. The positive influence of girdling on olive flowering and fruit set has been reported by Hartmann (1950) whereas, Ben-Tal and Lavee (1984) improved number of perfect flowers and yield in olive with girdling. The effect of girdling on tree growth, fruit quality and yield has been well documented in deciduous fruit crops (Noel, 1970; Grierson *et al.*, 1982; Goren *et al.*, 2004 and Wargo *et al.*, 2004).

2.2.1 Effect on growth

Abo-Taleb (1998) investigated the effect of girdling on productivity of olive cv. Picual tree. Girdling (single cut of 1 mm width, double cuts of 1 mm width, whole girdle of 20 mm width, 3/4 girdle of 20 mm width) done in December, January and February. All the girdling treatments decreased leaf pigment contents (chlorophyll a, b and carotene) compared to the control. The treatments significantly decreased leaf N content when compared with either the control or whole girdled branches. The leaf P content exhibited an opposite trend. The amount of K did not differ from the control.

Ungerer and Steyn (2009) studied the effect of scoring and GA_3 application during full bloom on fruit set and yield in 'Triumph' persimmon. Treatments consisted of an untreated control, application of GA_3 (20 mg L^{-1}) at 30% and 70% full bloom, scoring with girdling pliers in a complete circle around the trunk 10 cm above the graft union at 30% full bloom and combination of GA_3 and scoring. Scoring decreased one-year-old shoot growth significantly as compared to control. Scoring in combination with GA_3 also decreased vegetative growth as compared to control. In another study on the effect of trunk girdling on growth, fruit characteristics and reserve accumulation in late maturing persimmon it was found that girdling reduced trunk and shoot growth, occurrence of water sprouts as compared to control (Choi *et al.*, 2010).

2.2.2 Effect on flowering and fruit set

Sanghavi (1966) obtained an increase in fruit set of Bhokri and Italian Eliquina grapes with girdling done immediately after full bloom. Lavee *et al.* (1983) while studying the effect of girdling in adult table olive trees found that girdling in most cases caused an increase in the number of inflorescences. Fontanazza *et al.* (1987) observed that tying branches 3-4 cm in diameter with iron wire or girdling increased fruit set but did not decrease ovary abortion in olive cv. Ascolana Tenera.

Manzanillo olive trees were girdled at monthly intervals from 15th December to 15th April, removing 10 mm-wide rings of bark. In a separate trial, trees of the same cultivar growing under similar conditions were girdled by removing a 5, 10 or 15 mm wide ring of bark in April, i.e. a month before full bloom. Ungirdled trees served as controls. Girdling date had no significant effect on either flowering or fruit set (Lopez and Suarez, 1990).

Girdling has been reported to result in reduction of photosynthetic activity and also decrease in chlorophyll content according to Proietti and Tombesi (1990) which they attributed to the elevated starch concentration in the leaves. They concluded that from cultivation point of view, in olives, girdling cannot be considered a general remedy to overcome cases of scarce production. Rather, it should be used for very particular aims and only on single branches because reducing the photosynthetic rate cause an overall energy impoverishment.

Barut and Eris (1993) studied the effect of girdling, thinning and plant growth regulators on yield, quality and alternate bearing in olive cv. Gemlik. They found that girdling and GA_3 resulted in the highest number of panicles/shoot and fruit set/ panicle. Abo-Taleb (1998) investigated the effect of girdling on productivity of olive cv. Picual. Girdling was done in December, January and February. The treatments were single cut of 1 mm width, double cuts of 1 mm width, whole girdle of 20 mm width, 3/4 girdle of 20 mm width, and control. The single and double cuts of 1 mm width were most effective in enhancing the formation of flowers and promoted rapid healing. The single cut produced approximately twice as fruit set as did the control. The optimum time for girdling was in midwinter (December-February) prior to the major differentiation period.

However, Levin and Lavee (2005) reported that density of inflorescence in olive cultivars Barnea and Picual was not affected by girdling. In cultivars Picual and Souri significantly higher number of flowers per inflorescence on the girdled branches was recorded. Cultivars Barnea and Picual showed an increase in the percentage of perfect flowers on the girdled scaffolds. No such increase was observed in Souri cultivar. A significant increase in fruit set and yield was observed in girdled scaffolds.

Chanana and Gill (2006) reported that thinning, girdling and their combination advanced fruit maturity by 4-14 days in peaches. Also, different girdling treatments did not show any adverse effect on plant health and productivity as satisfactory healing of girdled ring took place in 28-34 days. Ungerer and Steyn (2009) studied the effect of scoring and GA_3 application during full bloom on fruit set and yield in 'Triumph' persimmon. Scoring with or without GA_3 application significantly improved fruit set as compared to the untreated control and GA_3 application.

Rivas *et al.* (2010) studied the effect of branch girdling on fruit-let abscission and its relationship with abcissic acid (ABA) and carbohydrate content in adult trees of 'Clementine' mandarin (*Citrus reticulata* Blanco). They reported that girdling reduced

ABA content in fruitlets by more than 60%, seven days after treatment. This decrease in ABA level was followed by a reduction in the rate of fruit-let abscission, which remained at levels significantly lower until 60 days after treatment. Final fruit set of leafless inflorescences was not affected by girdling, whereas leafy inflorescence reduced abscission at the end of physiological fruit drop. They concluded that girdling can improve fruit set by early modification of carbohydrates and GA/ABA relationship. Choi *et al.* (2010) found that trunk girdling (removing a ring of bark, 1 cm wide at 15 cm above the graft union) in April nearly doubled the fruit set and also enhanced fruit colour in persimmon cv. Fuyu.

2.2.3 Effect on fruit quality and yield

Favourable effect of girdling on berry size and subsequently the bunch size of grapes was observed in different cultivars of grapes (Sarowa and Bakshi, 1972; Bhujbal and Chaudhari, 1972; Bhujbal and Wavhal, 1972). They further reported that both cane or trunk girdling was effective. Whereas, Bhujbal and Chaudhari (1973) found cane girdling to be superior to arm or trunk girdling in increasing the berry size and cluster weight in Thompson Seedless grapes.

Manzanillo olive trees were girdled by removing 5, 10 or 15 mm wide ring of bark in April, i.e. a month before full bloom. Removing a 15 mm band of bark at 30 days before full bloom increased individual fruit weight from 3.9 g in the un-girdled control to 4.7 g (Lopez and Suarez, 1990). Girdling in combination with GA_3 has been reported to increase the fruit weight, flesh: seed ratio and yield of olive cv. Gemlik (Barut and Eris, 1993). Levin and Lavee (2005) observed the influence of girdling on flower type, number, inflorescence density, fruit set, and yield in three different olive cultivars (Bernea, Picual, and Souri). They did not find any positive effect of girdling on fruit size. A significantly higher yield in the girdled trees was recorded in all three cultivars.

Ahmad *et al.* (2005) reported an increase in berry weight, size and yield after girdling, and girdling plus GA_3 treatments in Perlette grapes. Chanana and Gill (2006) reported that both girdling alone and girdling plus thinning improved the fruit size and weight in peach, however, combination of girdling and thinning gave better results. Steyn *et al.* (2008) obtained increased return bloom, fruit set and yield in 'Triumph' persimmon after girdling and scoring. Scoring increased yield over two seasons by 61% compared to untreated control and by 92% compared to industry standard GA_3 application.

Ungerer and Steyn (2009) stated that scoring increased cumulative yield over two years by 61% compared to untreated control and by 114% compared to GA_3 treatment. Scored trees showed reduced fruit size compared to control. Similarly, Choi *et al.* (2010) also found no significant effect of girdling on fruit size of persimmon. The girdling treatments significantly decreased leaf N content in olive, when compared with control. The leaf P content exhibited an opposite trend. The amount of K did not differ from the control (Abo-Taleb, 1998).

2.3 STUDIES ON USE OF GROWTH RETARDANTS

Plant growth retardants are commonly used in fruit crops to modify the tree's vegetative growth and improve fruit setting and yield. The process of flower bud formation and flowering in young and mature trees is of vital concern to fruit growers. It has been universally accepted that plant bio-regulators exercise an indirect influence on flowering through their effect in restricting vegetative growth (Williams, 1973). The plant bio-regulators have been known to alter the indigenous balance of various hormones in favour of flowering and thus, regulate flowering in fruit crops (Luckwill, 1970). In fruit crops, a delicate balance exists between vegetative growth and fruiting. Frequently, this balance is disrupted due to sub-optimal weather or errors of orchard management resulting in vigorous growth that is detrimental to fruit quality, productivity, and profit margins. Plant growth retardants are commonly used in a great variety of fruit crops to modify the tree's vegetative growth and improve fruit setting and yield (Rademacher, 2000; Miller and Tworkoski, 2003). The current status of relevant information is reviewed here under:

2.3.1 Paclobutrazol

The growth retardant paclobutrazol (2R, 3R + 2S, 3S) - 1 - (4-chlorophenyl) -4, 4-dimethyle -2- (1, 2, 4 - triazol -1, yl) pentan-3-01 abbreviated as PP333 or cultar is a triazol compound having plant growth regulating properties. It is a potent inhibitor of gibberellin biosynthesis (Rademacher, 1995) and thus it has been regarded as a controlling agent in fruit crops (Quinlan and Webster, 1982; Tukey, 1983; Erez, 1984). The effect of paclobutrazol has been evaluated in many fruit crops. The reported responses range from growth retardation to enhanced flowering, yield, improved fruit quality, and better performance under environmental stresses.

2.3.1.1 Effect on growth

Swietlik and Miller (1985) observed that 'Golden Delicious' apple seedlings treated with paclobutrazol (0.1, 0.2, 0.4, 0.8, and 1.6 kg of a.i ha $^{-1}$) showed a decreasing trend in shoot growth rate, leaf area, and total dry weight with increasing rates of paclobutrazol. In Leccino another cultivar of olive, Antognozzi and Catalano (1985) found that trees of olive cv. Ascolana Tenera sprayed at full bloom or petal fall with paclobutrazol (1000 or 2000 ppm) or benzyl adenine (50 ppm) and paclobutrazol (1000 ppm) reduced shoot length. Curry and Williams (1986) observed application of different doses of paclobutrazol reduced vegetative growth in Top Red delicious apple by 80-90% and in Beurre d'Anjou pear by 90% as compared to control.

Porlingis and Voyiatzis (1986) observed that soil or foliar application of paclobutrazol (500-4000 mg/litre) on two-year-old potted plants of olive cultivar Hondrolia Halkidikis, reduced shoot growth, number of nodes, and inter-node length, and at the highest concentration caused bending of the main shoot. Similarly, Antognozzi and Preziosi (1986) also observed that foliar application of paclobutrazol (1500-5000 ppm) reduced plant height, shoot length, number of internodes and total leaf area, but increased shoot number in olive cv. Leccino. Costa *et al.* (1986) found that in a 5-year-old trees of nectarine cv. Independence, the final shoot length, leaf number and inter-node length was appreciably reduced by paclobutrazol (1, 2 or 4 kg/ha) applied after leaf drop.

In *Citrus unshiu* trees, Hu *et al*. (1988) found that application of paclobutrazol through soil (2, 4 or 6 g/tree), or foliar spray (1000, 1500 or 2000 ppm) on the new shoots of 2-3 cm reduced shoot lengths by 67.2, 59.8 and 50.9%, and 68.3, 62.9 and 62.2% in the respective treatments as compared to control whereas, mean leaf area was 15.1, 13.7 and 12.1 cm^2, and 16.8, 14.9 and 12.7 cm^2, respectively, as compared to control where the mean leaf area of 22 cm^2 was recorded.

Gaash and David (1989) applied paclobutrazol as a soil drench to intensively grown young or mature trees was effective in restricting shoot growth. Paclobutrazol (2-4 g per tree) applied under the canopy in spring or autumn retarded the upright growth of the vigorous cultivars Delmas and Western Schley cultivars of pecan, and they further observed the effect of paclobutrazol on the pecan trees during succeeding 2-3 years and found a more pronounced effect on Wichita and Mohawk cultivars of pecan.

Antognozzi and Frenguelli (1989) observed that single dose of paclobutrazol applied through soil or foliar application on two-year-old self-rooted olive cv. Leccino at the start of vegetative activity reduced tree height, shoot length, inter-node number and length, total leaf area, and the ratio between epigeal and hypogeal growth. However, the number of fruit clusters per tree were increased. They concluded that soil application and the combined soil and foliar application were most effective in lowering photosynthetic rate as well as leaf carbohydrate content.

In a study on the effect of paclobutrazol on growth of rooted cuttings of olive cultivars Arbequina and Manzanillo, Navarro *et al*. (1989) observed that longitudinal growth of plants of both the cultivars was retarded, but not completely inhibited by paclobutrazol (1.36 µM) when added to the nutrient solution. The plants treated with paclobutrazol continued their growth for 71 days of experimentation however, the growth rate was lesser than control. They also found that reduction of shoot growth in Arbequina olive plants was due to reduction of intermodal length, but the number of internodes remained the same. Although, there was non- significant effect of paclobutrazol on chlorophyll content of the leaves, but the leaf area was reduced from 4.44 cm^2 in control to 3.69 cm^2 in plants treated with paclobutrazol. They concluded that paclobutrazol is a weak growth retardant in olive in the sense that a substantially higher concentrations were required to obtain some of the effects observed in other fruit trees.

Hao *et al*. (1991) observed that five-year-old plants of Golden Delicious apple when sprayed with paclobutrazol (500, 1000 or 1500 ppm) or daminozide (2500 ppm) inhibited shoot growth and increased leaf thickness, leaf area and chlorophyll content at the higher concentrations but did not affect leaf number. In potted fig cv. El-Sultani transplants sprayed twice at monthly interval in May and June with chlormequat or paclobutrazol, each at 0, 500 or 1000 ppm, Abo-Rawash *et al*. (1991) observed an increase in the thickness of cuticle and epidermis with increasing growth retardant concentration. They reported that the number and size of stomata and palisade and spongy mesophyll cells, the size of intercellular air spaces, mid-vein depth and the area of vascular bundles decreased significantly when growth retardant concentration was increased from 500 to 1000 ppm.

In peach trees, Cao and Zhang (1992) observed that the vegetative growth of shoots was inhibited by paclobutrazol applied in spring and autumn as soil applications of 0.25-$1.0\ g/m^2$ and foliar sprays of 250-1000 ppm. They further observed that inhibitory effects of paclobutrazol on vegetative growth were positively correlated with the application rate. Werner (1993) studied the influence of paclobutrazol on growth and leaf nutrient content of mango cv. Blanco. He stated that soil application of paclobutrazol (750, 1500 or 2250 mg/tree) was more effective in reducing plant height (13.5 cm), internode length (0.6 cm), number of lateral shoots (2.1) and leaf size ($40\ cm^2$) compared with 45.8 cm, 1.1 cm, 3.5, $45\ cm^2$ for respective growth parameters under foliar application (750, 1125 and 1500 ppm). They also found that with the increase in concentration of paclobutrazol, the effect on the vegetative characteristics became more pronounced.

Similarly, Lavee and Haskal (1993) observed that the height and width of three-year-old olive cv. Muhasan trees reduced by 10-12%, as compared to control, by soil application of paclobutrazol (1 or 3 g /tree). Wang _et al._ (1993) found that in peach cultivars Maixang and Qingfeng, foliar and soil application of paclobutrazol applied @ 2000 ppm and $0.2 - 0.3\ g/m^2$, respectively in mid-May reduced the shoot length by 20-60%, shoot internode length by 15-40% and tree height by 15-30% as compared to control.

Zhu _et al._ (1994) studied the effect of paclobutrazol on vegetative growth and yield of walnut (_Juglans regia_) and concluded that foliar application of paclobutrazol (2000 ppm) and soil drenching with paclobutrazol 3g/tree reduced vegetative growth and increased the yield of walnut. They observed that the most effective time for application of paclobutrazol was during early shoot growth. They further reported that better results were achieved when paclobutrazol was applied twice as soil drench than the foliar spray. On the contrary, Helail and Eissa (1997) reported that spraying mango seedling shoots with paclobutrazol (2000 ppm) or TIBA (100 ppm) effectively enhanced root and shoot branching and improved growth parameters as well as increased N, Ca, Mg, Fe and Zn content in mango leaves.

Kumar _et al._ (1998) reported that foliar application of chlormequat (1000 mg/litre) or paclobutrazol (250 mg/litre) to grapes cv. Arkavati, one month after winter pruning led to a reduction in shoot length, leaf area and lowered the levels of endogenous gibberellin content in shoot tips. Tao _et al._ (1998) investigated effect of ethrel (1000 mg/litre), paclobutrazol (1000 mg/litre) and maleic hydrazide (500 mg/litre) spray on shoot growth and flower bud formation of 5-year-old 'Fuji' apple trees' and observed that paclobutrazol and ethephon reduced the shoot growth rate of trees to 57.83 and 71.20 per cent, respectively.

Hoda _et al._ (2001) reported that foliar (500, 1000 and 2000 ppm) as well as trunk soil line pour application (5 and 10 g a.i/tree) of cultar in mango cv. Langra reduced the length of terminal shoots and effects were more pronounced during the off year. They observed minimum length of terminal shoot (9.32 cm) with paclobutrazol when applied at the rate of 10 g a.i/tree whereas, maximum shoot length of 12.55 cm in untreated trees. Kumar _et al._ (2005) studied the effect of foliar sprays of chlormequat (500, 1000 and 1500 ppm) and paclobutrazol (500, 1000 and 1500 ppm) on the growth, yield and fruit quality of peach cv. Paradelux and reported that paclobutrazol (1500 ppm) was most effective in reducing the plant height, extension growth and shoot internode length.

Jacyna (2007) reported that 15 mg paclobutrazol cm^{-2} tree trunk cross-sectional area (TCSA) applied to 'Bing' sweet cherry by painting onto tree trunk bark in bands 10, 20, 30 or 40 cm wide reduced shoot growth to 55.5% and 21.1% of control trees in the year of application and in the next year, respectively. In both the years, TCSA, total shoot extension growth, shoot length, and tree height were visibly inhibited by the application of paclobutrazol. They further reported that one year after chemical application, the number of water sprouts diminished more than in the previous year. Asin *et al.* (2007) while studying the effect of paclobutrazol, prohexadione-Ca, deficit irrigation, summer pruning and root pruning on shoot growth in 'Blanquilla' pear found that single foliar application of paclobutrazol (250 cc hl^{-1}), 20 days after full bloom was most effective for reducing shoot length with a relative decrease of 25% in comparison to control.

Chanana and Gill (2007) found that soil application of paclobutrazol (2, 4, 6, and 8 g a.i/tree) significantly decreased trunk girth, tree height, tree spread and leaf area of Earli Grande cultivar of peach, with increasing concentrations of paclobutrazol. They recorded minimum trunk girth (5.18 cm), tree height (0.33 m), tree spread (0.91 m) and leaf area (27.87 cm^2) with paclobutrazol (8 g a.i./tree) as compared to 8.94 cm, 1.04 m, 1.31 m and 31.45 cm^2 for respective parameters under control. In another study on Shan-e-Punjab peach spaced at 6.0 x 1.5 m, Singh and Chanana (2007) reported that soil application of paclobutrazol (15 ml tree^{-1}) proved to be most effective in reducing the growth in terms of tree height (3.66 m), tree spread (1.22 m) and shoot length (53.38 cm) as compared to 4.56 m, 1.48 m, and 89.99 cm for respective parameters in control.

An investigation made by Kumari and Mankar (2008) on the effect of soil application of paclobutrazol (5.0, 7.5, and 10 g a.i tree^{-1}) in mango cv. Langra, revealed a marked reduction in vegetative growth *viz.*, length of terminal shoot (9.04 cm), number of leaves per shoot (9.15) and leaf area per shoot (628.66 cm^2) compared to 13.12 cm, 11.34 and 698.68 cm^2 of respective parameters in control. Chitu *et al.* (2008) also observed that spray of paclobutrazol (3000 ppm) reduced the vegetative growth of pear trees by 35% in 'Beurre Bosc' cultivar and by 42% in 'Triumph' cultivar as compared to untreated plants.

Siqueira *et al.* (2008) reported that with the increase in concentration of paclobutrazol (0, 75, 150 and 225 mg a.i. plant^{-1}) in 'Volkameriano' lemon there was a proportionate reduction in the stem length and diameter, length of the internodes and leaf area. Mobli and Baninasab, (2008) found that paclobutrazol spray (500 and 1000 ppm) significantly increased leaf chlorophyll content of *Prunus amygdalus and P. webbii* seedlings as compared with the control.

Arzani *et al.* (2009) studied the effect of paclobutrazol applied as soil drench at the rate of 0.5, and 1.5 g a.i tree^{-1} to 'J.H. Hale' and 'Red Skin' cultivars of peach and found that paclobutrazol significantly reduced vegetative growth in terms of shoot growth, and trunk cross sectional area of the trees. Leaf N and P was not influenced by any paclobutrazol treatments, but they recorded an increase of Ca and K concentrations in leaf. Burondkar *et al.* (2009) reported that among the various chemicals i.e. NAA, CPPU paclobutrazol, putrescine, KNO_3, K_2SO_4 and Ca-EDTA, each sprayed at 3 stages of fruit growth i.e. full bloom, marble and egg stages on 32-year-old mango cv. Alphonso, paclobutrazol treated trees had significantly higher leaf chlorophyll content.

Chitu *et al.* (2009) reported that foliar spray with paclobutrazol (0.2%), reduced shoot length in plum to 10.8 cm in Tuleu Gras variety and 16.6 cm in Stanley variety compared to 28.4 cm in the control. Negi and Sharma (2009) observed that paclobutrazol (500, 1000, 2000 ppm) applied through foliage at full bloom to 'July Elberta' peach (*Prunus persica* Batsch) resulted in a greater reduction in tree volume and pruning wood weight (kg) in trees given higher doses of paclobutrazol as compared to control.

In date palm, a monocotyledonous fruit tree, paclobutrazol has been reported to restrict the elongation rate of leaves and reduce the leaf length, thereby restraining trunk growth without affecting fruit quality or yield. Minimum number of new leaves (11.50) and average leaf length of (27.53 cm) was recorded in trees supplied with paclobutrazol (6.25 g a.i/tree), whereas maximum values of 14.25 and 79.14 cm, respectively were recorded in control trees (Aloni *et al.*, 2010). In olive, Sharma *et al.* (2011) obtained maximum reduction in vegetative growth in terms of shoot growth (10.40 cm) and leaf area (5.30 cm^2) with the application of paclobutrazol (2000 ppm) as compared to control. They also observed that paclobutrazol tended to decrease the stomatal size but increased stomatal density from 25.75 to 30.58 per microscopic field in leaves.

2.3.1.2 *Effect on flowering and fruit set*

Greene (1986) observed that post-bloom foliar application of paclobutrazol (1500 or 3000 ppm) increased flesh firmness and reduced seed number and fruit size at harvest in Delicious apples. In the following year after application, they found that the flowering was not affected but fruit set was increased. The effect of foliar application of paclobutrazol (250-2000 ppm) on vegetative growth, fruiting, and carbohydrate levels and movement in 'Williams Bon Chretien' pear trees was studied by Sansavini *et al.* (1988) and found that paclobutrazol (1000 ppm), sprayed 20 days after petal fall, reduced shoot growth by 20-30%, increased flower bud differentiation, and promoted fruit set in the following year.

Antognozzi *et al.* (1989) observed that foliar application of paclobutrazol (1000, 2000 or 5000 ppm) in olive cultivar Leccino controlled vegetative activity and increased floral initiation. In mango, Khader *et al.* (1989) found that application of paclobutrazol (2500 and 5000 ppm) resulted in delay in panicle development and flowering in mango and increased flowering percentage. Menzel and Simpson (1990) reported that paclobutrazol application reduced flushing and increased flowering in litchi. Khader (1991) reported that spray of 2000 ppm paclobutrazol to mango cv. Dashehari reduced plant height, trunk girth, the number of new shoots, internode length and increased the percentage flowering.

An increase in flowering, fruit set and yield was observed in five-year-old plants of Golden Delicious apple sprayed with paclobutrazol (500, 1000 or 1500 ppm) or daminozide (2500 ppm) by Hao *et al.* (1991). On the contrary, Jones *et al.* (1991) observed no consistent effect of paclobutrazol (50, 100 or 200 mg/litre), applied in combination with ethephon (200 mg/litre) on flowering and fruit set of Red delicious apples in the following spring. They concluded that though no significant differences occurred between any of the paclobutrazol concentrations, or timing, all treated trees yielded more than the untreated trees. Further, they stated that when ethephon was used in combination with paclobutrazol, fruit set was similar to that with paclobutrazol alone, however, highest fruit set was obtained with paclobutrazol sprayed at the rate of 100 mg/litre.

Goguey (1992) found that the rate of fruit set increased and the number of inflorescence decreased, with the application of paclobutrazol in mango trees. Kurian and Iyer (1993) obtained early and profuse flowering, enhanced proportion of hermaphrodite flowers in response to soil drenching with paclobutrazol (2.5, 5.0 or 10.0 g/tree) in mango cv. Alphonso. They also observed that fruit set was promoted by 2.5 g paclobutrazol/tree. Fruit retention was not promoted by any of the treatments, but the highest paclobutrazol rate had a detrimental effect on both fruit set and retention.

Manifold increase in mango production has been reported by the application of paclobutrazol due to increase in intensity of flowering, higher percentage of perfect flowers and better fruit set by Burondkar and Gunjate (1993). In lemon cv. Eureka, spray of paclobutrazol (300-450 ppm) significantly enhanced flower-bud formation, increased the proportion of normal inflorescences and also increased fruit set in the following year (Qin *et al.*, 1994).

A comparison between soil and foliar application of paclobutrazol made by Pan *et al.* (1995) revealed that foliar application was more effective in respect of advancement and intensity of flowering in loquat. Chen *et al.* (1995) also observed that paclobutrazol application as a soil drench or foliar spray had a pronounced effect on early flowering in peach seedlings and also increased the mean number of flower buds per tree.

Salazar and Vazaquez (1997) reported that increasing rate of paclobutrazol application increased the earliness of flowering in mango trees. Tao *et al.* (1998) investigated the effect of ethrel, paclobutrazol and maleic hydrazide spray on 5-year-old 'Fuji' apple trees' shoot growth and flower bud formation. They found that paclobutrazol was the most effective for inducing flower bud formation up to the extent of 306.79% and increased leaf chlorophyll content in the following year.

Porlingis and Voyiatzis (1999) observed that paclobutrazol decreased the harmful effect of high temperatures on fruit set in olive trees in the potted plants of olive cultivars Amphissis and Chalkidikis. They found that trees of olive cv. Amphissis exposed outdoors to a maximum temperature of 32 °C during flowering and 35 °C for one week after its termination, and trees treated with paclobutrazol showed higher fruit set (23.1%) than the untreated control trees (12.6%). Exposure of cv. Chalkidikis trees to a maximum temperature of 35 °C during flowering and 37 °C afterwards resulted in 1.4 and 14.8% fruit set in control and paclobutrazol treated plants, respectively. They concluded that the paclobutrazol induced tolerance in olive trees to high temperature and possibly to low relative humidity, which in turn ensured a satisfactory fruit set.

Application of paclobutrazol resulted in profuse flowering and increased proportion of pistillate and perfect flowers in mango (Singh *et al.*, 2000). Whereas, a reduction in the flowering season of litchi was reported by Wu *et al.* (2000) with paclobutrazol application. Paclobutrazol application also resulted in profuse flowering in treated trees, which culminates into a higher fruit set and yield in litchi (Faizan *et al.*, 2000). Similar findings on the effect of paclobutrazol on flowering of mango have been reported by Hoda *et al.* (2001), who found that soil application of paclobutrazol (5 g a.i/tree) induced profuse flowering with highest flowering shoots (36.20%) and fruit set (44.06%) as compared to 18.23% and 26.37%, respectively in control.

Blaikie *et al.* (2004) studied the effect of morphactin and paclobutrazol on flowering of mango cv. Kensington Pride and found that both morphactin and paclobutrazol applications resulted in profuse flowering. They also observed that maximum intensity of flowering was attained in paclobutrazol treated trees, reaching levels in excess of 90% at most sites. In Dashehari mango trees, Singh *et al.* (2005) found that among different plant growth regulators, foliar application of NAA (100 and 200 ppm), TIBA (100 and 200 ppm) and chlormequat (500 and 1000 ppm) as spray and paclobutrazol (5 and 10 g a.i./tree) as soil drench, soil application of paclobutrazol (5 and 10 g a.i./tree) considerably increased the percentage of panicles and hermaphrodite flowers, and fruit yield.

In an attempt to induce regular and early fruiting in mango, Singh and Ranganath (2006) observed that soil application of paclobutrazol (5 ml/l per tree) increased percentage of shoots flowered, reduced number of days taken for flowering, number of fruits per panicle, and fruit retention in mango cv. Banganapalli as compared to control. Similarly, in mango cv. Gulabkhas, soil application of paclobutrazol (5 g a.i. per tree) was found to be most effective in inducing more number of flowering shoots and improving the fruit set and fruit retention during the off-year (Singh and Singh, 2006).

Chusri *et al.* (2008) observed that paclobutrazol applied in the 'Irwin' mango as soil drench (1 g a.i. per tree), or as a foliar spray (1500 ppm) advanced bud break by 18-22 days as compared to untreated trees. They also recorded more than 96 per cent of the paclobutrazol treated trees produced floral shoots, compared with only 35 per cent in control trees. Enhancement in flowering in response to paclobutrazol was obtained by Cruz *et al.* (2009), who found that paclobutrazol (400, 800, and 1200 mg per plant) applied to 'Tahiti' acid lime plants increased the number of flowers by 137% in irrigated plants and 371% in those kept under water stress, as compared to control.

Arzani *et al.* (2009) found that soil application of paclobutrazol (0.5 and 1.5 g a.i tree[-1]) advanced flowering and time of fruit harvest in 'J.H. Hale' and 'Red Skin' peach cultivars by 2-4 and 2-7 days, respectively. They further reported that paclobutrazol application increased flower as well as fruit set, crop density, yield and yield efficiency in both cultivars in the following season. Kumbhar *et al.* (2009) while comparing the efficacy of use of cultar and austar (both commercial formulations of paclobutrazol) in mango production, found that both the products caused an earliness of flower initiation by 3-4 weeks as compared to control.

Brar and Bal (2010) reported that maximum flowering and fruit set was recorded in paclobutrazol treated plants in both rainy and winter crops of guava cv. Allahabad Safeda and also found that plants at wider spacing responded better to paclobutrazol application. Mouco *et al.* (2010) observed that paclobutrazol treated mango plants flowered 25 days earlier as compared to control and 15 days earlier as compared to Pro-Ca (prohexadione-calcium) and chlormequat treated plants. They further reported that paclobutrazol treated plants exhibited the highest flowering percentages, with over 70 per cent of the marked branches showing panicles. Saini and Sharma (2010) reported that foliar application of paclobutrazol (1000 and 2000 ppm) in mid-October and mid-November significantly increased fruit set in the trees of plum cv. Red Beaut as compared to untreated trees.

Sharma *et al.* (2011) reported that paclobutrazol (2, 4 and 6 g a.i. tree^{-1}) as soil application, and foliar application (500, 1000 and 2000 ppm) significantly improved blooming intensity, percentage of perfect flowers and fruit set in olives as compared to control. They further observed that soil application of paclobutrazol (4 g a.i/tree) resulted in maximum blooming intensity (1.15%), proportion of perfect flowers (46.73%) and fruit set (7.61%), as compared to 0.45%, 37.88% and 3.46%, respectively in control.

2.3.1.3 *Effect on fruit quality and yield*

Swietlik and Miller (1985) observed that total N, Zn, and Cu absorbed by Golden Delicious apple seedlings was not affected whereas K, Ca, Mg, and Mn decreased with paclobutrazol treatments. Curry and Williams (1986) reported that the application of paclobutrazol (1.0, 2.0 or 4.0 g /tree) in 'Rainier' cherry trees advanced anthesis by about three days as compared to control. They further found that total fruit yield increased by 33% with paclobutrazol (1.0 g/tree) and 105% with paclobutrazol (4.0 g/tree), but the average fruit size decreased by 20 per cent.

Costa *et al.* (1986) found that paclobutrazol (1, 2 or 4 kg/ha) applied after leaf drop, in five year old trees of nectarine cv. Independence, increased yield/tree with all the concentrations of paclobutrazol, whereas the average fruit weight increased only with the application of 1 Kg/ha paclobutrazol. Mavrodiev *et al.* (1987) also reported that soil application of cultar (1.2 and 2.4 g a.i tree^{-1}) in peach resulted in 46.9% and 39.4% increase in yield, respectively over control. Paclobutrazol also increased the fruit size and number. In 'Flavorcrest' peach trees, Martin *et al.* (1987) observed that soil application of paclobutrazol increased the cumulative yield from 30.1 t/ha in control to 41.8 t/ha with paclobutrazol application, without measurable fruit quality loss.

Beneficial effects of paclobutrazol have been reported in high density planting of Japanese plum, where soil application of paclobutrazol controlled excessive vegetative growth and promoted flower and fruit production (Gaash *et al.*, 1989). In pecan trees, paclobutrazol applied as a soil drench to intensively grown young/ mature trees effectively increased yield and also increased the nut size (Gaash and David, 1989). Paclobutrazol applied on 4-year-old Gola pear trees increased leaf P, Ca and Mg contents and also increased the number of fruits/tree, whereas soil application of paclobutrazol resulted in an increase in fruit production compared with control (Bist, 1990).

In Japanese plum, Chandel and Jindal (1991) found that paclobutrazol (500 ppm) sprayed either at full bloom or at pit hardening stage significantly increased fruit set from 14.06 to 21.86% and yield from 64.50 to 71.00 kg/tree. They also observed that trees sprayed with paclobutrazol (250 ppm) produced fruits having highest average length, diameter, and weight.

Koodziejczak and Tymoszuk (1992) reported that soil application of paclobutrazol (1g/tree) in autumn resulted in highest total fruit yields (50.2 kg/tree) and lowest (13.8 kg/tree) with foliar application of paclobutrazol (0.1%) in Stanley plum. Paclobutrazol application had no significant effect on fruit size but foliar application of paclobutrazol increased fruitlet drop. Cao and Zhang (1992) reported that the individual fruit weight and yield/tree of peach was greatly increased by soil application of paclobutrazol (0.5 g/m^2) and percent flower formation at the nodes also increased. They concluded that foliar spraying was more effective than soil application and autumn application was less effective than spring application in peach.

In a study on 10-year-old trees of olive cultivars Manzanillo and Barnea trees, paclobutrazol (2, 4 or 6 g tree^{-1}) applied through soil in February for two consecutive years, increased yield by about 20% in Manzanillo and Barnea. However, application of paclobutrazol (6 g tree^{-1}) did not increase yield during the two treatment years, but resulted in the highest yield in the third year, when no paclobutrazol was applied (Lavee and Haskal, 1993). In mango cv. Blanco, Werner (1993) found that the leaf content of N, Ca, Mn, Zn and B contents were increased while P, K and Cu contents were decreased with the soil and foliar application of paclobutrazol.

In mango, soil drenching with paclobutrazol (2.5 and 5.0 g/tree) considerably increased fruit yield but reduced when paclobutrazol was applied at the rate of 10 g/ tree. Soil drenching with paclobutrazol (2.5 g/tree) during November and March in alternate years for regulating tree size and improving yield in young bearing mango trees was recommended by Kurian and Iyer (1993). Burondkar and Gunjate (1993) reported 2.6 times increase in yield from 101.87 fruits/tree to 274.19-287.98 fruits/ tree in Alphonso ciltivar of mango, without affecting fruit size and quality following paclobutrazol application through soil (5 and 10 g/tree) or foliar sprays (500, 1000 and 2000 ppm), during July and August each year for three successive years. They also concluded that foliar application of paclobutrazol was less effective as compared to soil application.

Zhu *et al.* (1994) reported that high concentrations of paclobutrazol (2000 ppm for foliar sprays and 3 g for soil drench) applied twice reduced vegetative growth and increased the yield in walnut. The most effective time for application was during early shoot growth. They further reported that soil drench was more effective method of application than the foliar spray. Proetti and Tombesia (1996) observed that soil application of paclobutrazol markedly increased the extent of flowering and yield of olive in the following year.

In mango, paclobutrazol (4 g per tree) increased the number of fruits and yield as well as produced high quality fruits when applied as a soil drench in the first year after treatment. However, the effects wore off by the third year, indicating that paclobutrazol needs to be applied annually to increase mango fruit yields (Yadav and Singh, 1998). Foliar application of growth retardants cycocel (1000 mg/litre) or paclobutrazol (250 mg/litre) to grape cv. Arkavati, one month after winter pruning has been reported to improve fruit set, number of berries/bunch, and bunch weight (Kumar *et al.*, 1998).

Abou-Rawash *et al.* (1998) reported that post bloom foliar spray of paclobutrazol (300 ppm) resulted in highest fruit weight and pulp weight in Taimour mango trees. Porlingis *et al.* (1999) observed that application of paclobutrazol resulted in a marked increase in the fruit set and yield of olive. Faizan *et al.* (2000) found that paclobutrazol application resulted in profuse flowering, which culminated into a higher fruit set and yield in litchi. Kumar *et al.* (2005) reported that cultar (1500 ppm) sprayed on trees of peach cv. Paradelux increased the fruit number and yield, but had no significant effect on fruit weight.

Singh and Bhattacherjee (2005) observed that paclobutrazol significantly increased fruit yield up to 50.67 and 41.40 kg/tree respectively in Chausa and Langra cultivars of mango with paclobutrazol (6 g a.i/tree) as compared to 7.12 kg/tree in untreated trees. However, in Dashehari mango fruit yield of 68.90 kg/tree was recorded with paclobutrazol (4 g a.i/tree). They further observed that during the third year when the paclobutrazol dose was reduced to half, only half of the highest concentration (8 g a.i/tree) was found to cause yield enhancement in cultivars Chausa and Langra. In Dashehari also, half dose of paclobutrazol (2 g a.i/tree) was found to be significantly effective in increasing the fruit yield. They concluded that Dashehari responded better to paclobutrazol treatments than Langra and Chausa. Residual effect of paclobutrazol was also observed only in cv. Dashehari when its application was not done during the third year.

Singh and Ranganath (2006) reported that soil application of paclobutrazol (5 ml/l per tree) in mango cv. Banganapalli, resulted in maximum number of fruits per panicle at harvesting stage and number of fruits per tree as compared to control. Singh and Singh (2006) obtained highest yield of 70.50 and 68.70 kg per tree during the off-year in mango trees with soil application of paclobutrazol at the rate of 5 and 10 g a.i. per tree, respectively. Soil treatment with paclobutrazol also improved the fruit quality attributes.

In Shan-e-Punjab cv. of peach, Singh and Chanana (2007) recorded maximum fruit weight (81.98 g) with soil application of paclobutrazol (15 ml tree[-1]) followed by 79.06 g with paclobutrazol spray (1000 ppm), whereas minimum fruit weight of 72.23 g in control. They also found that soil application of paclobutrazol (15 ml/tree) produced highest yield of 23.66 kg/tree as compared to 16.46 kg/tree recorded in untreated plants. Jain and Dashora (2007) recorded highest yield with foliar application of paclobutrazol (500 ppm) in guava cv. Sardar, as compared to other treatments *viz.*, NAA (100 and 200 ppm), ethrel (250 and 500 ppm), paclobutrazol (250 ppm), chlormequat (500 and 1000 ppm) and triacontanol (5 and 10 ppm). Carreno *et al.* (2007) observed that paclobutrazol (1.0, 2.0, 2.5 and 3.0 ml/plant) applied through ferti-irrigation in grape cv. Napoleon, increased the size of the berries and number of bunch per stem.

Reddy and Kurian (2008) applied paclobutrazol as foliar sprays (500, 1000 or 2000 ppm) or soil drench at 5 or 10 g a.i. per tree in Alphonso mango trees during September for three consecutive years. They found that application of paclobutrazol as soil drench was more effective than its foliar spray and doubled fruit yield during the six years of observation. However, average weight of a fruit was less in the case of paclobutrazol treated plants. Chusri *et al.* (2008) observed that paclobutrazol applied to soil by drenching with 1 g a.i. per tree, or as a foliar spray (1500 ppm) in the 'Irwin' mango resulted in higher fruit yield per tree as compared to control.

Arzani *et al.* (2009) found that paclobutrazol application increased yield and yield efficiency in both cultivars in the following season in 'J.H. Hale' and 'Red Skin' peaches. However, fruit size was smaller in the paclobutrazol treated trees than control. The leaf N and P was not influenced by any paclobutrazol treatments, but Ca and K concentrations were increased by paclobutrazol (1.5 g a.i tree^{-1}). Chitu *et al.* (2009) observed that paclobutrazol (0.2%) resulted in the highest fruit yield of 37.1 and 46.1 kg per tree as compared to 20.7 and 19.8 kg per tree in untreated Tuleu Gras and Stanley plants, respectively. Negi and Sharma (2009) reported that foliar application of paclobutrazol (500, 1000, 2000 ppm) at full bloom to 'July Elberta' peach (*Prunus persica* Batsch) resulted in higher average fruit yield as compared to control.

Burondkar *et al.* (2009) studied the influence of plant growth regulators NAA (20 ppm), CPPU (10 ppm) and paclobutrazol (10 and 25 ppm), polyamine putrescine (50 ppm), and nutrients KNO$_3$ (1.0%), K$_2$SO$_4$ (1.0%) and Ca-EDTA (0.1%), each sprayed at 3 stages i.e. full bloom, marble and egg stages of fruit growth and soil application of paclobutrazol (750 mg/m canopy diameter), irrigation along with absolute control, was investigated on 32-year-old mango cv. Alphonso. Among all the treatments, paclobutrazol (25 ppm) and putrescine (50 ppm) recorded significantly higher yield (107.7 and 101.74 kg fruits/tree) over the control (48.32 kg/tree). Anez (2009) reported that paclobutrazol alone or in combination with ammonium thiosulphate exerted a positive effect on the number of fruits/tree, fructification index (number of fruits/m^2) in second year after application in mango cv. Haden. Similarly, Kumbhar *et al.* (2009) recorded significantly more number of fruits per tree following paclobutrazol application as compared to control.

Brar and Bal (2010) reported that paclobutrazol (500 and 1000 ppm) sprayed on guava cv. Allahabad Safeda resulted in significantly higher fruit number, fruit yield, yield efficiency, fruiting density compared to ethephon treated and control plants. The guava plants treated with paclobutrazol and ethephon assimilated significantly higher N, P, Zn and Fe content in leaves. However, the leaf K concentration was reduced with paclobutrazol treatments.

Mouco *et al.* (2010) reported that treatments with paclobutrazol resulted in highest per plant production in mango cv. Kent. They also found that paclobutrazol alone or in combination with ProCa, advanced maturity of fruits by 25 days. Saini and Sharma (2010) reported that foliar application of paclobutrazol (1000 ppm) in mid-November improved yield as compared to untreated trees of plum cv. Red Beaut, however, the fruit size and weight were decreased with the application of paclobutrazol.

Sharma *et al.* (2011) observed highest fruit yield (6.87 kg/tree), reduction in fruit drop by 21.77% with maximum fruit length (21.11 mm) and fruit breadth (13.68 mm) in olive with paclobutrazol application as compared to 5.34 kg/tree, 61.19%, 20.47 mm and 13.06 mm, respectively in control.

2.3.2 Chlormequat

The growth retardant chlormequat (2-chloroethyl trimethyl ammonium chloride) also known as cycocel (CCC) has been found to reduce the height without any malformation of shoot growth and also stimulates the fruit bud formation, fruit set and other physiological processes in a plant. According to Rademacher (1995) the reduction in shoot growth occurs due to reduction in elongation as well as by lowering the rate of cell division with the application of cycocel in plants.

2.3.2.1 Effect on growth

In mango cv. Langra, cycocel application considerably reduced linear growth by 38% and diameter of shoots by 94% of control and the shoot growth was completely ceased in August (Choudhari and Rudra, 1971). In another cultivars of mango, Maiti *et al.* (1972) observed that cycocel significantly retarded linear increase of shoots in young as well as mature Langra and young Baramasia mango. They noticed that growth reducing effect of cycocel was more pronounced in mature trees than in young ones wherein retardation in linear extension of shoots of young as well as mature mango trees was maximum with cycocel applied at the concentration of 2000 ppm in case of mature Langra and at 4000 ppm in case of young plants of Langra and Baramasia.

Chundawat and Gupta (1974) sprayed different concentrations of chlormequat ranging from 1000 to 4000 ppm on phalsa and observed progressive reduction in the number of nodes from 15.6 to 14.5, leaf area from 44.58 to 34.83 cm^2 and total shoot length from 87.6 to 52.4 cm However, Forlani and Rotundo (1974) reported that application of cycocel (2000 to 6000 ppm) in the month of June and August did not show its dwarfing effects on olive cv. Coratina. Nicotra *et al.* (1977) reported that with the spray of cycocel (10000 ppm) twice (60 and 90 days after bloom) on Doyenne Du Comice cultivar of pear there was a remarkable reduction in the vegetative growth and also noticed that when cycocel was sprayed on the top part of the tree, it allowed almost regular growth of the shoots in the lower part of the tree thereby indicating its effects being localized to the portion of the plant where it is applied.

In 40-year-old mango cv. Mulgoa, Suryanarayana and Rao (1978) observed that spray of daminozide or chlormequat, each at 5000 ppm enhanced leaf thickness and increased the number and length of palisade cells. They further observed a reduction in the number of stomata and an increase in their size with both the growth retardants but the effect of chlormequat was more pronounced than that of daminozide. Nicotra (1979) reported that with the application of chlormequat (10000 ppm) for eight consecutive years, there was a reduction upto 43 and 69 per cent in tree volume and height, respectively in Comice cultivar of pear. In mango cv. Langra, reduction of shoot length, diameter and number of leaves per shoot has been obtained by Rath and Das (1979) with the application of cycocel (3000 mg/l) in combination with ringing.

Suryanarayana (1981) observed that in mango cv. Mulgoa trees sprayed with chlormequat or daminozide, each at 5000 ppm, at monthly intervals between May and January, the levels of chlorophyll and carotenoids consistently increased in chlormequat treated leaves. Kathiravetpillai and Kulasegaram (1981) also reported that spray of CCC (6000 ppm) on 5-month-old plants of tea also increased leaf chlorophyll content and enhanced N, P and K contents of the leaves.

Rai and Tewari (1986) evaluated the physiological effects of daminozide, chlormequat and 2,4,5-T in pear (*Pyrus communis* L.) cv. Victoria and observed retarded shoot extension growth, early cessation of extension growth, increased spur formation and leaf chlorophyll content. A marked decrease in shoot length after application of cycocel on different cultivars of apple has also been reported by many workers (Soczek and Zaziabi, 1978; Hircovskey and Gajdosechova, 1984; Bliek 1985).

Embree *et al.* (1987) reported that the trees receiving two foliar sprays of chlormequat (1000 ppm) reduced terminal growth, leaf area and fruit stem length in pear cv. Clapp's Favourite. Abo-Rawash *et al.* (1991) also found that cycocel and paclobutrazol application each at 0, 500, 1000 ppm showed an increase in number and size of stomata in fig. Kurian and Iyer (1993) observed that during the first vegetative flushing in mango after the imposition of treatments, all levels of paclobutrazol and higher levels of alar and cycocel, resulted in shorter shoots, reduced leaf area and per cent increase in plant height.

Ramteke and Somkumar (2005) found that chlormequat (500 ppm) sprayed at 5+5+3+3 leaf stage with topping and side shoot removal in Tas-A-Ganesh cultivar of grapes significantly reduced the mean shoot length from 198.70 cm to 155.13 cm. They also recorded reduction in number of leaves and leaf size with chlormequat (500 ppm) applied at 5+5+3 leaf stage with no topping and side shoot removal and chlormequat (500 ppm) applied at 5+5+3+3 leaf stage with no topping and side shoot removal.

Sharma *et al.* (2011) applied cycocel (500, 1000, and 2000 ppm) in olive cultivars Leccino and Cannino, and observed significantly reduced shoot growth ranging from 13.51 to 13.26 cm and leaf area from 5.32 to 5.30 cm^2 as compared to untreated plants wherein mean shoot growth of 16.84 cm and leaf area of 5.44 cm^2 was recorded by them.

2.3.2.2 Effect on flowering and fruit set

Pre-bloom application of chlormequat to the foliage was found to increase fruit set in grapes by more than 20 per cent (Coombe, 1965; Skene, 1969). It was reported by Garg and Singh (1970) that pre-bloom application of cycocel at 250-1000 ppm resulted in earlier flowering in mango. Choudhari and Rudra (1971) reported a significant increase from 3.6 per cent to 92.0 percentage of flowering shoots with application of cycocel (5000 ppm) as compared to control trees of mango cv. Langra. Maiti *et al.* (1972) also found that cycocel application ranging from 1000 to 4000 ppm reduced vegetative growth and promoted flowering in mango.

In different cultivars of grapes, application of cycocel has been found to increase fruit set. According to Bajwa *et al.* (1977) CCC (500 ppm) was optimum to increase fruit set in Himrod variety of grape, while Farmahan (1971) observed CCC (300 ppm) to be adequate for increasing fruit set in Thompson seedless. Dhillon and Sharma (1973) found 1000 ppm of CCC to be optimum for increasing fruit set in Perlette, while Armugam and Madhavarao (1973) observed 2000 ppm to be optimum for Anab-e-Shahi grapes.

Grauslund (1974) also reported that cycocel at 0.2 per cent was effective in promoting flowering and fruit set in pear. Mukhopadhyay (1976) found that chlormequat (5000 ppm) applied seven times starting in mid-May, significantly increased the production of panicles and the size of panicles and hermaphrodite flowers in mango cv. Langra. Blinovskii *et al.* (1980) found that cycocel at 0.6 or 1.2 per cent induced formation of flower buds and improved fruit set in apple.

In mango cv. Mulgoa spray with chlormequat or daminozide each at 5000 ppm at monthly intervals between May and January resulted in an increase in the number of flowering shoots consistently higher levels of leaf chlorophyll and carotenoids content as reported by Suryanarayana (1981). In 13-year-old Dashehari mango trees, Daulta *et al.* (1981) observed that chlormequat (500 or 1000 ppm) had no appreciable effect on flower type (staminate, pistillate or hermaphrodite) but chlormequat (500 ppm) increased fruit set upto 0.32 per cent as compared to control where fruit set was only 0.08 per cent .

In Langra cultivar of mango, Rath *et al.* (1982) reported that spray of several growth regulators on the ringed main branches in mid October and again in early November during "off" years increased flowering and the best results were obtained with cycocel (3000 ppm) which gave 90, 89 and 81 per cent flowering in the "off", "on" and "off" years, respectively, compared with 8, 67 and 2 per cent in the control for respective years. In kagzi lime trees, Desai *et al.* (1982) observed that cycocel (1000 ppm) sprayed in mid-August and again in mid-September followed by 2,4,5-T (10 ppm) in late September increased flowering from 16.3% to 58.2%. They further reported that the trees which flowered in October produced a desirable off-season crop in May.

In olive cv. Picual, Hegazi and Stino (1982) obtained a noticeable increase in the percentage of perfect flowers with kinetin (100 mg/litre) or chlormequat (200 mg/litre) whereas, in another cultivars of olive Blanquetta, Serrana and Picual application of ethephon (200 mg/litre), chlormequat (200 mg/litre) or daminozide (2000 mg/litre) considerably increased the percentage of perfect flowers. However, all these treatments stimulated bud burst and flower bud formation in cv. Blanquetta.

Yamamoto (1983) reported that spray of cycocel 1000 or 2000 ppm hastened the appearance of flower clusters and increased flowering in young loquat trees. Sinha *et al.* (1983) reported that application of daminozide and chlormequat each at 500-2000 ppm at pit hardening stage in peach cv. Alexander advanced maturity and increased fruit set in the following year by 71 to 83 per cent compared to control.

Khader and Rao (1984) observed that application of chlormequat (500, 1000 and 1500 ppm) to grape cultivars Anab-e-Shahi, Muscat and Bangalore Blue resulted in more number of flowering shoots, highest number of infloresences per spur and fruiting shoot as compared to control and the effect increased with increasing concentrations.

In litchi cultivars Deshi and Purabi, trees sprayed with GA_3 (50 and 100 ppm), NAA (25 and 50 ppm), 2,4,5-T (25 and 50 ppm), maleic hydrazide (200 and 300 ppm), chlormequat (1000 and 2000 ppm), ethephon (50 and 100 ppm) or water (control) on five occasions between September and January, Thakur *et al.* (1989) reported that chlormequat (2000 ppm) produced the highest number of hermaphrodite flowers/panicle and lowest sex ratio (male: hermaphrodite) in both cultivars. They also obtained increased fruit set with the application of cycocel at different concentrations.

In Alphonso cultivar of mango, Ravishankar *et al.* (1993) tested various chemicals *viz.*, TIBA at 100 or 150 ppm, Ethrel (ethephon) at 250 p.p.m. either alone or with 1% KNO_3 or 1% urea, CCC (chlormequat) at 500 or 1000 ppm, Alar (daminozide) at 500 or 1000 ppm, and Atonik (nitroguaiacol + nitrophenolate) at 1:1000 either alone or with 1% urea, to compare the effectiveness of different growth regulators for inducing flowering in the off-year on shoots that had borne a crop in the previous season and concluded that the only compound which proved most effective in inducing flowering on new vegetative shoots that developed subsequently on fruited shoots was CCC whereby induction was 25.7 and 21% with 500 and 1000 ppm, respectively.

Atawia and Hassan (1995) observed that spray of 2000 ppm cycocel in mid May to LeConte pear enhanced flowering in the following year. Sehrawat *et al.* (1998) found that spray of chlormequat (1500 ppm) on Thompson Seedless grapes at full bloom increased berry set from 41.94% to 54.85%. Theron *et al.* (1998) sprayed chlormequat (1000, 2000, 3000 or 4000 mg/litre) on pear cultivar Doyenne du Comice and reported improvement in number of flowers/bud, fruit set and yield. They also observed no significant change in the fruit drop pattern although fruit set appeared to be higher in treated trees.

Nambisan *et al.* (2007) studied the effects of chlormequat (100, 150 or 200 ppm), NAA (10, 20 or 30 ppm), 2,4-D (10, 20 or 30 ppm) and GA_3 (10, 20 or 30 ppm) on the yield of sapota cv. Kalipatti and observed an increase in fruit set with the increase in concentration of the growth regulator. However, the highest number of flowers per shoot of 13.8 and 13.9 was obtained with 200 ppm CCC and 30 ppm 2,4-D, respectively. Thirugnanavel *et al.* (2007) revealed that application of GA_3 (50 ppm) in June and cycocel 1000 ppm in September followed by spray of KNO_3 2% in october resulted in delaying of flowering, increased number of flowers per shoot, initial fruit set, fruit retention, number of fruits and yield in acid lime.

In plum cv. Red Beaut, Saini and Sharma (2010) observed that foliar application of chlormequat (1000 and 2000 ppm) in mid-October and mid-November resulted in an increase in fruit set as compared to untreated trees. Similarly, in olive cultivars Leccino and Canino, Sharma *et al.* (2011) observed that application of chlormequat

(500, 1000 and 2000 ppm), a month before flowering significantly increased blooming intensity, proportion of perfect flowers and fruit set with the increase in concentration of chlormequat.

2.3.2.3 Effect on fruit quality and yield

Chundawat and Gupta (1974) recorded highest fruit yield in phalsa with B-nine at 4000 ppm followed by cycocel 4000 ppm whereas Hricovsky (1978) reported that application of cycocel 40, 70 and 100 days after petal-fall in apple cv. Ontario and Starkrimson Delicious, decreased the growth of one-year shoots, gave a significant increase in fruit yield. Bajwa (1979) reported that two sprays of chlormequat 2000 ppm, first 20 days before full bloom and second 10 days later gave the best results with regard to reducing flower bud drop and increasing the total number of bunches/ vine from 420 in control to 581.

Nicotra (1979) reported that Comice pear trees sprayed with chlormequat 10000 ppm for eight years almost doubled in yield efficiency (accumulated yield/final tree volume), while Spadona di Salerno trees sprayed for five years gave an increase of 30% in cumulative yield as compared to unsprayed trees. He opined that the effect appeared to be due to better fruit set. Daulta *et al.* (1981) obtained a considerable improvement in fruit size (10.30 x 5.60 cm) and weight (171.30 g) with the application of cycocel (1000 ppm) as compared to control wherein they recorded fruit of 9.40 x 5.40 cm size and 147.30 g weight. They also recorded highest pulp: stone ratio in fruits obtained from trees treated with 500 ppm cycocel (6.48) and minimum in control (5.63).

Tesu *et al.* (1983) found that chlormequat (2000 and 4000 ppm) retarded shoot growth and stimulated flowering, bud formation, fruiting and yield in the pear cv. Clapp's Favourite. The highest yield (104.8 kg/tree or 88 t/ha) was recorded with chlormequat (4000 ppm) applied in November followed by chlormequat (2000 ppm) applied in April and GA_3 (50 ppm) applied in July. Kumar and Singh (1984) reported that in Thompson Seedless vines chlormequat (250 ppm) gave the best results with regard to fruit set, bunch weight and size, berry weight and size.

A negative effect of chlormequat on the fruit yield of pear cultivars Merton Pride, Clara Frijs, Fondante de Charneu and Doyenne du Comice was obtained by Grauslund (1983). He found that chlormequat (1000 ppm and 2000 ppm) sprayed once or twice a year for six years reduced the total fruit yield/tree by 10-26 kg/tree compared with control where yield of 74-102 kg/tree was recorded. He also reported more Ca and less K in leaves of treated trees as compared to control trees. Ben and Kropp (1986) observed that spraying Jonathan apple trees with chlormequat (5000 ppm), either once in mid July or twice in mid June and mid July, significantly increased mean fruit weight.

Rai and Tewari (1986) reported that daminozide, cycocel and 2,4,5-T retarded shoot extension growth which resulted in early cessation of extension growth, increased spur formation and leaf chlorophyll content, and reduced fruit drop, fruit weight and size in pear cv. Victoria. They also found that cycocel (2000 ppm) and daminozide (2000 ppm) increased fruit firmness and delayed ripening by about a week. In another study carried out by Kovaleva and Cherevko (1986) reported that chlormequat sprayed twice at 0.5% to young pear cv. Vicar of Winkfield and Dekanka Zimnyaya retarded vegetative growth and advanced flowering and fruiting by two years, thus shortening the non-bearing period and reducing pruning requirements in young orchards.

Kilany *et al.* (1986) applied GA_3, CCC (chlormequat) and alar (daminozide) alone or in combination to 'Ghariby' grapes. They obtained highest fruit set (40.5-41.5%) with chlormequat (200 ppm) at full bloom whereas bunch weight was highest when GA_3 at 20 ppm, applied 10 days before full bloom, followed by either chlormequat or daminozide, both at 200 ppm, applied at full bloom. Mohammad *et al.* (1987) also reported that CCC (500, 1000 or 1500 ppm) applied 7-10 days before full bloom to grape cv. Roomy Red, significantly increased vine yield, number of berries/cluster, and cluster weight over control.

Guha (1993) reported that application of 0.6% cycocel on 5-year-old apple cv. Golden Delicious trees, significantly increased fruit set and yield/tree in the second year of application compared with the control. Atawia and Hassan (1995) reported that cycocel sprays (1000 or 2000 ppm) in LeConte pear trees at full bloom increased leaf N, Ca, Fe and Zn contents as compared with controls.

Ramteke and Somkumar (2005) observed that cycocel (500 ppm) applied once, twice, thrice or four times significantly improved yield per vine in Tas-A-Ganesh grapes grafted on Dogridge rootstock. They recorded highest yield of 10.80 kg/vine with the application of cycocel at 5+5+3+3 leaf stage with topping and removal of side shoots and lowest in control (0.613 kg/vine). They also recorded improved berry weight (143.8 g), berry diameter (14.9 mm) and length (22.3 mm) with cycocel application at 5+5+3+3 leaf stage with no topping and removal of side shoots, as compared to control.

Dutta *et al.* (2008) reported that in mango cv. Himsagar, NAA, GA_3 and cycocel (chlormequat) application significantly increased the fruit yield, individual fruit weight and size of the fruit compared with the control whereas, Mahalle *et al.* (2010) revealed that the yield in terms of number of fruits/tree and weight of fruits/tree was maximum with the application of two sprays of 1000 ppm cycocel at an interval of one month before initiation of flowering.

Mouco *et al.* (2010) found that though the difference in fruit yield of mango cv. Kent was not significant among treatments but the Pro-Ca and CCC concentration higher than 3.0 g a.i plant^{-1} increased fruit mass of 15.7 and 10.8%, respectively as compared to control. Agrawal and Dikshit (2010) reported that application of chlormequat (200 and 400 ppm) in sapota cv. Cricket Ball at flower bud differentiation significantly improved fruit length (15.49 and 15.60 cm), fruit diameter (84.13 and 85.85 cm), fruit weight (6.09 and 6.16 g), volume (79.37 and 81.76 cc) and pulp weight (68.51 and 69.40 g) as compared to 14.96 cm, 77.11 cm, 5.74 g, 70.10 cc and 65.20 g for respective parameters in control. Saini and Sharma (2010) observed that spraying plum cv. Red Beaut trees with CCC (1000 ppm) in mid-November increased fruit yield whereas, it decreased fruit size and weight as compared to control.

Sharma *et al.* (2011) reported that foliar application of CCC (500, 1000 and 2000 ppm) significantly increased mean fruit yield from 5.34 kg/tree to 6.05 kg/tree, fruit size from 20.47 x 13.06 mm to 21.04 x 13.54 mm, and reduced fruit drop from 61.19% to 47.13% in olive.

CHAPTER 3
MATERIALS AND METHODS

The present investigation "Response of girdling, micro-nutrients and growth retardants on olive (*Olea europea* L.) cv. Frontoio" was carried out at private orchard located at Dharamthal, District Udhampur, Jammu & Kashmir, India during 2008-09 and 2009-10. The details about the experimental site, material and the methodology adopted during the course of these investigations are presented under following sub-heads.

3.1 CLIMATE AND WEATHER CONDITIONS

The experimental orchard at Dharamthal (Udhampur) is situated in the intermediate zone at latitude $32^0 50^/$ North and longitude $74^0 55^/$ East. The altitude of the place is 1100 meter above mean sea level. Annual precipitation is about 910 mm mostly coinciding during February to June (about 80 per cent). The mean annual maximum and minimum temperature are 21.72^{0}C and 12.57^{0}C, respectively. Summer months are mildly hot with temperature and humidity ranging from 16.51 to 28.25 ^{0}C and 37.9 to 97.32 per cent, respectively. The winter months experience mild cold conditions with an average temperature ranging from 4.76^{0}C to 17.17^{0}C. January is the coldest month, when minimum temperature touches to 4.76^{0}C. The highest temperature is recorded in the month of June (28.25^{0}C).

3.2 SOIL OF THE EXPERIMENTAL PLOT

In order to study the physical and chemical characteristics of the soil of experimental orchard, soil samples were collected from different places with the help of soil auger at 0-90 cm depth. Soil samples of different locations were mixed together, air dried and was finally grinded to powder form for analysis. Initial soil status of experimental orchard with regard to mechanical and chemical properties was recorded and is presented in Table 1.

Table 1: Initial status of mechanical and chemical composition of soil.

Particular	Contents	Method used
A. Mechanical analysis		International Dispersion Method (Piper,1950)
Sand (%)	32	
Silt (%)	28	
Clay (%)	40	
B. Chemical analysis		
pH	6.4	1:2 soil water suspension (Jackson, 1973)
Electrical conductivity	0.24	1:2 soil water suspension (Jackson, 1973)
Organic carbon (%)	0.87	Walkley and Black's Method (Piper, 1966)
Available Nitrogen (Kg ha^{-1})	283	Alkaline Potassium Permanganate Method (Subbiah and Asija, 1956)
Available Phosphorus (Kg ha-1)	73	Stannous chloride reduced ammonium molybdate method (Jackson, 1973).
Available Potassium (Kg ha-1)	188	Flame photometer (Merwin and Peech, 1951)

The data in the Table 1 indicate that the texture of the soil was clay loam and soil was almost neutral in reaction. The available nitrogen and potassium were in medium range 283 and 188 Kg ha^{-1}, respectively) while available phosphorus was in high range (73 Kg ha^{-1}).

3.3 EXPERIMENTAL DETAILS

Uniform, healthy and disease free, 15 years old olive trees spaced 8m x 5 m apart were selected for the investigations (Plate 1). All cultural management practices were followed as per the package of practices of SKUAST-J.

3.3.1 Experiment I : Effect of girdling and foliar application of micronutrients on growth and fruitfulness of olive cv. Frontoio.

Total number of treatments = 17

T_1	:	Control
T_2	:	Girdling
T_3	:	0.4% $ZnSO_4$
T_4	:	0.5% $ZnSO_4$
T_5	:	0.6% $ZnSO_4$
T_6	:	0.4% Boric acid
T_7	:	0.5% Boric acid
T_8	:	0.6% Boric acid
T_9	:	0.4% $ZnSO_4$ + 0.4% Boric acid
T_{10}	:	0.4% $ZnSO_4$ + 0.5% Boric acid
T_{11}	:	0.4% $ZnSO_4$ + 0.6% Boric acid
T_{12}	:	0.5% $ZnSO_4$ + 0.4% Boric acid
T_{13}	:	0.5% $ZnSO_4$ + 0.5% Boric acid

T_{14}	:	0.5% $ZnSO_4$ + 0.6% Boric acid
T_{15}	:	0.6% $ZnSO_4$ + 0.4% Boric acid
T_{16}	:	0.6% $ZnSO_4$ + 0.5% Boric acid
T_{17}	:	0.6% $ZnSO_4$ + 0.6% Boric acid
Number of replications	:	03
Design of experiment	:	Randomized Block Design (RBD)
Number of trees per replication:		01

All the bearing branches of the trees were girdled by removing 10 mm wide rings of bark, one week before full bloom. Both the nutrients were sprayed in the first week of March and repeated 30 days after the first spray, during both the years of investigation.

3.3.2 Experiment II: Effect of growth retardants on growth and productivity of olive cv. Frontoio.

Total number of treatments: 10

T_1	:	Control	Water spray
T_2	:	Paclobutrazol	2 g a.i tree^{-1}
T_3	:	Paclobutrazol	4 g a.i tree^{-1}
T_4	:	Paclobutrazol	6 g a.i tree^{-1}
T_5	:	Paclobutrazol	500 ppm
T_6	:	Paclobutrazol	1000 ppm
T_7	:	Paclobutrazol	2000 ppm
T_8	:	Chlormequat	500 ppm
T_9	:	Chlormequat	1000 ppm
T_{10}	:	Chlormequat	2000 ppm
Number of replications	:	03	
Design of experiment	:	Randomized Block Design	
Number of trees per replication	:	01	

Soil application of Paclobutrazol was given in the month of December whereas, foliar application of paclobutrazol and chlormequat was done in the month of March and repeated 30 days after first application, during both the years of investigation.

3.4 METHODOLOGY ADOPTED

3.4.1 Preparation of chemical formulation for foliar application

The desired concentration of zinc sulphate and boric acid (AR grade) were prepared by dissolving their required quantity in a small quantity of water and the final volume was made up by adding required volume of water. Different concentrations of boric acid solution were prepared by dissolving it in a small quantity of warm water and then required volume was made up by adding desired quantity of water.

The required quantity of paclobutrazol (PP_{333}) as cultar was dissolved in a small quantity of water and then required volume was made up by adding additional quantities of water. The desired concentration of chlormequat as cycocel were prepared by dissolving required quantity of chemical in small amount of water and then desired volume was made of by adding additional quantity of water.

Plate 1: A view of experimental site.

3.4 METHODOLOGY ADOPTED

3.4.1 Preparation of chemical formulation for foliar application

The desired concentration of zinc sulphate and boric acid (AR grade) were prepared by dissolving their required quantity in a small quantity of water and the final volume was made up by adding required volume of water. Different concentrations of boric acid solution were prepared by dissolving it in a small quantity of warm water and then required volume was made up by adding desired quantity of water.

The required quantity of paclobutrazol (PP_{333}) as cultar was dissolved in a small quantity of water and then required volume was made up by adding additional quantities of water. The desired concentration of chlormequat as cycocel were prepared by dissolving required quantity of chemical in small amount of water and then desired volume was made of by adding additional quantity of water.

3.4.2 Growth characteristics

3.4.2.1 Trunk circumference

Trunk diameter of olive trees was measured at 15 cm above the ground with the help of digital vernier callipers (Mitutoyo, Japan made) and expressed in centimeters (cm). The data is presented in terms of per cent increase in trunk circumference over their initial values recorded at the beginning of the experiment.

Trunk circumference = 2ðr (r = radius of tree trunk)

3.4.2.2 Shoot extension growth

Twenty uniform and healthy shoots were randomly selected all over the tree canopy in all directions. The length of each shoot was measured at the beginning and end of growing season between the points of initiation of new growth to the extremity of the shoot tip and expressed in centimetres.

3.4.2.3 Leaf area

For measuring leaf area, one hundred leaves were randomly sampled from all over the tree canopy of experimental trees and their cumulative area was recorded with the help of Leaf Area Meter, Systronics-211 model and expressed as average leaf area in square centimetres (cm^2).

3.4.2.4 Relative growth rate

Relative growth rate was determined by recording the initial shoot extension growth (L_1) and final shoot extension growth (L_2) at two times *viz.*, in the last week of March (t_1) and in the last week of August (t_2). Relative growth rate was then compared by using formula as suggested by West *et al.* (1920) and expressed as cm cm^{-1} $month^{-1}$.

$$\text{Relative growth rate} = \frac{LogL_2 - LogL_1}{t_2 - t_1}$$

Where,

L_1	=	Shoot length at time t_1
L_2	=	Shoot length at time t_2
t_1	=	Last week of March
t_2	=	Last week of August

3.4.3 Physiological parameters

3.4.3.1 Unit leaf area

In order to determine constant factor 'K' for the calculation of unit leaf area, hundred leaf samples were drawn at random from 15 years old trees of olive. The leaves were selected from all four main compass points of tree canopy. The length of the leaf (excluding petiole) was measured from base to top and breadth at the widest point. The product of the length x breadth was calculated. The actual leaf area was measured by using a leaf area meter. A regression equation *viz.*, Y = b. X was fitted for each type of leaf, where Y = predicted leaf area, b= the factor or constant 'K' and X= length x breadth. From this, factor 'K' was calculated by formula b = " XY / "X^2. The unit leaf area was calculated according to Sestak *et al.* (1971) by multiplying length x breadth with constant factor 'K'.

3.4.3.2 Specific leaf area

The specific leaf area (SLA) was calculated by dividing total leaf area (cm^2) by total leaf dry weight (g).

3.4.3.3 Leaf water content

Twenty five leaves were collected from all around the periphery of the experimental trees and immediately weighed. Then these leaves were separately kept in brown paper bags and dried in oven at 65± 5°C till constant weight was attained. The per cent leaf water content was calculated on fresh weight basis by the formula given below.

$$\text{Leaf water content (\%)} \quad = \quad \frac{W_1 - W_2}{W_1} \times 100$$

Where, W_1 = Initial fresh weight of leaf sample (g)

W_2 = Final oven dry weight of leaf sample (g)

3.4.3.4 Stomatal count

On the ventral surface of these leaves, a thin layer of quick fix is applied with the help of a fine camel brush. This layer of quick fix is allowed to dry for some time and after this, thin film of quick fix is carefully taken out from the leaf surface without causing any damage to the film. The strip of the film was then sub-divided into smaller pieces of convenient size and were fixed on a clean glass slide covered the sections with cover slip. Then seen under a microscope at a resolution of 10x. Stomatal density present in one microscopic field was then counted (Beakbane and Majumdar, 1975).

3.4.3.5 Chlorophyll content

Healthy, fully expanded leaves were collected in the morning hours, put in poly bags and placed in ice box and brought to laboratory. For estimation of total chlorophyll, the leaves were washed properly and chopped into fine pieces. One gram of the finely chopped leaves was extracted with 80 per cent acetone for chlorophyll extraction and the absorbance read at 645 nm and 663 nm with the help of a UV-1601 Visible Spectrophotometer SHIMADZU. Using the absorbance coefficients, the amount of chlorophyll was estimated by using the formula given by Arnon (1949).

$$\text{Total chlorophyll (mg/g)} \quad = 20.2\,(A_{645}) + 8.02\,(A_{663}) \times \frac{V}{100 \times W}$$

A_{645} = Absorbance at 645 nm
A_{663} = Absorbance at 663 nm
V = Volume of aliquot made
W = Weight of the leaf tissue taken

3.4.4 Flowering and fruit set

3.4.4.1 Time and duration of flowering

The data of time and duration of flowering was recorded for each treatment. The dates of beginning of flowering as evidenced by opening of first flower and end of flowering i.e. petal fall were recorded in the field. The duration of flowering was worked out by counting the number of days from beginning of flowering to end of flowering.

3.4.4.2 Blooming intensity

The blooming intensity of experimental trees was recorded in accordance with the method suggested by Westwood (1978).

$$\text{Blooming intensity} = \frac{\text{Number of flower buds}}{\text{Number of flower buds} + \text{Number of vegetative buds}} \times 100$$

3.4.4.3 Proportion of perfect flowers

For ascertaining proportion of perfect flowers, twenty five inflorescences were sampled from all sides of the experimental trees. The individual flowers of these inflorescences were carefully examined to determine their sex. These flowers were then categorized into two groups *viz.* perfect and staminate on the basis of presence or absence of a fully developed and functional pistil.

3.4.4.4 Fruit set

The extent of fruit set was computed by using the formula as suggested by Westwood (1978).

$$\text{Fruit set (\%)} = \frac{\text{Number of fruits}}{\text{Number of inflorescence}} \times 100$$

The initial observations on fruit set were recorded at four weeks after full bloom whereas final fruit set was recorded six weeks after full bloom, thus allowing sufficient time for abscission of unfertilized fruits.

3.4.4.5 Yield

The entire crop harvested from each tree was weighed and considered as total yield and expressed in kg tree^{-1}.

3.4.5 Physical characteristics of fruits

One hundred healthy fruits were randomly selected from each treatment to record observations on their physico-chemical characteristics.

3.4.5.1 Fruit size

The length and diameter of selected fruits was measured by using a digital vernier calliper in centimetres. The size was calculated as average of length and diameter and expressed in cm.

3.4.5.2 Fruit weight

The entire weight of a fruit sample was recorded on a top pan electrical balance with an accuracy of $\pm$ 0.5 g and average fruit weight was expressed in grams (gm).

3.5.5.3 Fruit volume

The volume of a fruit sample was estimated by water displacement method using a graduated glass cylinder and was expressed in 'cubic centimeters' (cc).

3.5.5.4 Pulp: stone ratio

The fruit flesh was separated from the stone and the ratio between weights of pulp and stone was worked out for all the treatments.

3.4.6 Oil content

Oil content of fruit pulp was estimated by Soxhlet Extraction method using hexane as a solvent (AOAC, 1980) and expressed in per cent on fresh weight basis.

3.4.7 Total leaf N, P, K, Ca and Mg

3.4.7.1 Leaf sampling

For estimation of macro-nutrient status of experimental trees, one hundred fully expanded leaves along with petioles were sampled from the middle portion of the previous season's shoots situated all around the canopy of the tree as recommended by Chapman (1964).

3.4.7.2 Preparation and storage of leaf samples

Cleaning, drying, grinding and storing of samples were carried out in accordance with the procedures outlined by Kenworthy (1964).

3.4.7.3 Estimation of N

For the estimation of N, 0.5 g of plant material was digested in 15-20 ml concentrated sulphuric acid in the presence of digestion catalyst as described by Jackson (1973). The aliquot thus derived was used for the estimation of total N by micro Kjeldahl method (AOAC, 1980).

3.4.7.4 Estimation of P, K, Ca and Mg

For the estimation of P, K, Ca and Mg digestion was done in triacid mixture containing concentrated nitric acid, perchloric acid and sulphuric acid in the ratio of 10:4:1. All precautions as suggested by Piper (1966) for wet digestion of leaf samples were taken. The volume of aliquot was made to 100 ml and filtered through Whatman no.1 filter paper.

Total P was determined by Vanadomolybdo phosphoric yellow colour method as described by Jackson (1973), while total K in the plant sample was estimated with the help of Corning 410 digital Flame photometer. Calcium and Magnesium were determined on Atomic Absorption Spectrophotometer.

3.4.8   Soil analysis

Soil samples from 0-45 cm depth were collected from the basin of each tree during the month of March for both the years. Four samples from each basin were taken and mixed to form one composite sample. The soil samples were air dried, ground and passed through 2 mm plastic sieve and stored in cloth bags for further analysis.

3.4.8.1   Soil pH

Soil pH was determined in 1:2 soil water suspension using Eltop digital pH meter

3.4.8.2   Organic carbon

Organic carbon was determined by Walkley and Black's rapid titration method as described by Piper (1966).

3.4.8.3   Available nitrogen

The available nitrogen was estimated by alkaline permanganate method as modified by Subbiah and Asija (1956).

3.4.8.4   Available phosphorus

The available phosphorus in the soil sample was extracted with 0.5 N sodium bicarbonate solution when pH was adjusted to 8.5 and then determined by Stannous chloride reduced ammonium molybdate method (Jackson, 1973).

3.4.8.5   Available potassium

The available potassium in the sample was extracted with 1 N ammonium acetate, (Merwin and Peech, 1951) after shaking 5 g of soil sample in 25 ml of extractant for 5 minutes and then filtered through whatman No. 1 filter paper. After filtration volume of aliquat was made to 50 ml and available K was determined on flame photometer.

3.4.9   Statistical analysis

The data generated from these investigations were appropriately computed, tabulated and analyzed statistically as per procedure described by Panse and Sukhatme (2000). The level of significance was tested for different variables at 5 per cent level of significance. The data of two years were pooled and analysed statistically using computer software.

CHAPTER 4

RESULTS

The results obtained from the present investigation on the "Response of girdling, micro-nutrients and growth retardants on olive (*Olea europea* L.) cv. Frontoio" carried out during the year 2008-09 and 2009-10 are presented under appropriate headings in this chapter.

4.1 EFFECT OF GIRDLING AND FOLIAR APPLICATION OF MICRONUTRIENTS (ZINC AND BORON) ON GROWTH AND FRUITFULNESS OF OLIVE CV. FRONTOIO.

4.1.1 Growth characteristics

The data pertaining to growth characteristics in terms of percent increase in trunk circumference shoot extension growth and relative growth rate is presented as under.

4.1.1.1 Increase in trunk circumference

The perusal of the data presented in Table 2 showed that during 2008-09 increase in trunk circumference ranged from 6.18 to 7.90 percent, wherein, maximum increase in trunk circumference (7.90%) was recorded in trees sprayed with 0.5% zinc sulphate in combination with 0.5% boric acid and minimum (6.18%) in untreated trees of olive. However, the effect of different treatments on percent increase in trunk circumference was non-significant. During the second year of experimentation also increase in trunk circumference was not significantly affected by girdling as well as foliar application of zinc and boron applied singly or in combination with each other, whereas maximum increase in trunk circumference (8.23%) was obtained with foliar application of 0.5% zinc sulphate in combination with 0.5% boric acid and minimum (6.63%) with foliar application of 0.4% zinc sulphate alone. In the pooled data also, the effect of different treatments was observed to be non-significant and the increase in trunk circumference ranged from 8.07 to 6.85 percent, exhibiting maximum value with foliar application of 0.5% zinc sulphate in combination with 0.5% boric acid and minimum with foliar application of 0.4% Zinc sulphate alone.

4.1.1.2 Shoot extension growth

The shoot extension growth was significantly influenced by girdling and micro-nutrient sprays of zinc and boron and the results obtained are presented in Table 2.

During 2008-09, maximum shoot extension growth (9.41 cm) was recorded in trees sprayed with 0.6% zinc sulphate in combination with 0.5% boric acid which was statistically at par with shoot extension growth recorded in trees sprayed with 0.6% zinc sulphate in combination with 0.4% boric acid (9.40 cm), 0.6% Zinc sulphate in combination with 0.6% boric acid (9.39 cm), 0.5% zinc sulphate in combination with 0.5% boric acid (9.22 cm), 0.5% zinc sulphate in combination with 0.6% boric acid (9.15 cm) and 0.5% zinc sulphate in combination with 0.4% boric acid (8.46 cm) whereas, minimum shoot extension growth (5.74 cm) was recorded in girdled trees.

However, during the second year (2009-10), shoot extension growth ranged from 6.46 cm to 8.44 cm with all the treatments tried under this study wherein maximum shoot extension growth (8.44 cm) was recorded with 0.6% zinc sulphate in combination with 0.6% boric acid and least shoot extension growth (6.46 cm) was recorded in girdled trees. Pooled data showed maximum shoot extension (8.92 cm) in trees sprayed with 0.6% zinc sulphate in combination with 0.6% boric acid. The treatments *viz.*, 0.6% zinc sulphate in combination with 0.5% boric acid, 0.6% zinc sulphate in combination with 0.4% boric acid, 0.5% zinc sulphate in combination with 0.6% boric acid, 0.5% zinc sulphate in combination with 0.5% boric acid and 0.5% zinc sulphate in combination with 0.4% boric acid were equally effective in registering shoot extension growth within the range of 8.18 cm to 8.90 cm. Minimum shoot extension growth (6.10 cm) was registered in girdled trees.

Table 2: Effect of girdling, zinc and boron on increase in trunk circumference, shoot extension growth and relative growth rate in olive cv. Frontoio.

Treatment	Increase in trunk circumference (%)			Shoot extension growth (cm)			Relative growth rate (cm cm^{-1} month^{-1})		
	2008-09	2009-10	Pooled	2008-09	2009-10	Pooled	2008-09	2009-10	Pooled
T_1	6.18	7.53	6.86	6.10	6.63	6.37	0.036	0.029	0.033
T_2	6.63	7.23	6.93	5.74	6.46	6.10	0.018	0.026	0.022
T_3	7.07	6.63	6.85	6.65	6.64	6.65	0.029	0.021	0.025
T_4	7.73	7.53	7.63	6.72	6.90	6.81	0.025	0.023	0.024
T_5	7.43	7.63	7.53	7.10	6.82	6.96	0.020	0.023	0.022
T_6	6.90	7.33	7.12	7.00	7.27	7.14	0.024	0.024	0.024
T_7	7.10	6.90	7.00	7.24	7.30	7.27	0.026	0.024	0.025
T_8	7.27	7.73	7.50	7.53	7.46	7.49	0.026	0.025	0.026
T_9	7.10	7.53	7.32	7.88	7.62	7.75	0.026	0.027	0.027
T_{10}	7.63	8.00	7.82	8.03	7.65	7.84	0.031	0.031	0.031
T_{11}	7.47	7.83	7.65	8.22	7.81	8.02	0.032	0.029	0.031
T_{12}	7.27	7.50	7.38	8.46	7.89	8.18	0.029	0.027	0.028
T_{13}	7.90	8.23	8.07	9.22	8.15	8.69	0.030	0.025	0.028
T_{14}	7.37	7.92	7.65	9.15	8.37	8.76	0.035	0.030	0.033
T_{15}	7.37	7.97	7.67	9.40	8.26	8.83	0.033	0.027	0.030
T_{16}	7.47	7.97	7.72	9.41	8.38	8.90	0.037	0.027	0.032
T_{17}	7.50	8.13	7.82	9.39	8.44	8.92	0.035	0.026	0.031
C.D $_{(0.05)}$	NS	NS	NS	1.11	1.35	0.86	0.007	NS	0.005

4.1.1.3 Relative growth rate (RGR)

The data on the effect of different treatments on relative growth rate embodied in Table 2 revealed that the highest relative growth rate (0.037 cm cm^{-1} month^{-1}) during 2008-09 was recorded in trees sprayed with 0.6% zinc sulphate in combination with 0.5% boric acid which was closely followed by untreated trees (0.036 cm cm^{-1} month^{-1}), spray treatment with 0.6% zinc sulphate in combination with 0.6% boric acid and 0.5% zinc sulphate in combination with 0.6% boric acid (0.035 cm cm^{-1} month^{-1}), 0.6% zinc sulphate in combination with 0.4% boric acid (0.033 cm cm^{-1} month^{-1}), 0.4% zinc sulphate in combination with 0.6% boric acid (0.032 cm cm^{-1} month^{-1}), 0.4% zinc sulphate in combination with 0.4% boric acid (0.031 cm cm^{-1} month^{-1}) and 0.5% zinc sulphate in combination with 0.5% boric acid (0.030 cm cm^{-1} month^{-1}) whereas, lowest RGR (0.018 cm cm^{-1} month^{-1}) was recorded in girdled trees. In the year 2009-10, RGR for different treatments ranged from 0.021 to 0.031 cm cm^{-1} month^{-1} and spray of zinc and boron applied singly or in combination with each other as well girdled plants showed non-significant effect on relative growth rate of olive trees. Pooled data showed highest relative growth rate of 0.033 cm cm^{-1} month^{-1} in trees sprayed with 0.5% zinc sulphate in combination with 0.6% boric acid and in untreated trees, whereas lowest shoot extension growth (0.022 cm cm^{-1} month^{-1}) was recorded in girdled trees and trees sprayed with 0.6% zinc sulphate alone.

4.1.2 Leaf area, unit leaf area and specific leaf area

4.1.2.1 Leaf area

The results presented in Table 3 reveal that spray of zinc and boron applied singly or in combination with each other significantly affected the leaf area of olive trees under study.

Table 3: Effect of girdling, zinc and boron on leaf area, unit leaf area and specific leaf area of olive cv. Frontoio.

Treatment	Leaf area (cm²)			Unit leaf area (cm²)			Specific leaf area (cm² g⁻¹)		
	2008-09	2009-10	Pooled	2008-09	2009-10	Pooled	2008-09	2009-10	Pooled
T_1	3.10	3.25	3.18	3.02	3.13	3.08	4.48	3.65	4.07
T_2	3.03	3.21	3.12	3.04	3.26	3.15	4.23	4.53	4.38
T_3	3.39	3.56	3.47	3.40	3.49	3.45	5.80	4.58	5.19
T_4	3.85	4.01	3.93	3.86	3.98	3.92	5.22	5.59	5.41
T_5	3.81	3.97	3.89	3.81	3.98	3.90	5.45	4.96	5.21
T_6	3.76	4.17	3.97	3.77	4.09	3.93	5.74	6.14	5.94
T_7	4.02	3.92	3.97	4.03	3.75	3.89	6.06	4.68	5.37
T_8	3.93	4.09	4.01	3.94	4.13	4.04	7.07	5.63	6.35
T_9	3.96	4.08	4.02	3.98	4.01	3.99	4.99	5.76	5.37
T_{10}	4.20	4.34	4.27	4.21	4.34	4.28	7.20	7.26	7.23
T_{11}	4.29	4.43	4.36	4.29	4.37	4.33	5.78	7.92	6.85
T_{12}	4.17	4.29	4.23	4.22	4.13	4.17	7.76	6.44	7.10
T_{13}	4.59	4.77	4.68	4.59	4.72	4.66	6.98	7.56	7.27
T_{14}	4.79	4.95	4.87	4.80	4.84	4.82	7.83	6.85	7.34
T_{15}	4.56	4.59	4.57	4.67	4.36	4.52	8.09	7.46	7.78
T_{16}	4.48	4.69	4.59	4.21	4.51	4.36	8.24	7.10	7.67
T_{17}	4.47	4.54	4.51	4.49	4.50	4.49	7.47	6.75	7.11
C.D $_{(0.05)}$	0.56	0.56	0.39	0.56	0.50	0.37	2.42	2.03	1.55

During 2008-09, maximum leaf area (4.79 cm^2) was observed in trees sprayed with 0.5% zinc sulphate in combination with 0.6% boric acid closely followed by trees sprayed with 0.5% zinc sulphate in combination with 0.5% boric acid (4.59 cm^2), 0.6% zinc sulphate in combination with 0.4% boric acid (4.56 cm^2), 0.6% zinc sulphate in combination with 0.5% boric acid (4.48 cm^2), 0.6% zinc sulphate in combination with 0.6% boric acid (4.47 cm^2) and 0.4% zinc sulphate in combination with 0.6% boric acid (4.29 cm^2) which were at par with each other, whereas minimum leaf area (3.03 cm^2) was measured in the girdled trees. During the second year of experimentation (2009-10) same pattern in respect of leaf area was observed wherein, maximum leaf area of 4.95 cm^2 was recorded in trees sprayed with 0.5% zinc sulphate in combination with 0.6% boric acid and minimum leaf area of 3.21 cm^2 was obtained in girdled trees of olive. The results in pooled analysis showed maximum leaf area of 4.87 cm^2 in trees sprayed with 0.5% zinc sulphate in combination with 0.6% boric acid closely followed by trees sprayed with 0.5% zinc sulphate in combination with 0.5% boric acid, 0.6% zinc sulphate in combination with 0.5% boric acid, 0.6% zinc sulphate in combination with 0.4% boric acid and 0.6% zinc sulphate in combination with 0.6% boric acid and were at par with each other, whereas minimum leaf area (3.12 cm^2) was observed in girdled trees closely followed by control (3.18 cm^2) and were at par with each other.

4.1.2.2 Unit leaf area

Perusal of the data presented in the Table 3 revealed that unit leaf area was significantly affected by different treatments tried during the first year of investigation exhibiting maximum unit leaf area (4.80 cm^2) with the foliar application of 0.5% zinc sulphate in combination with 0.6% boric acid closely followed by foliar application of 0.6% zinc sulphate in combination with 0.4% boric acid, 0.5% zinc sulphate in combination with 0.5% boric acid, 0.6% zinc sulphate in combination with 0.6% boric acid and 0.4% zinc sulphate in combination with 0.6% boric acid registering values of 4.67, 4.59, 4.49 and 4.29 cm^2, respectively and were at par with each other and minimum unit leaf area (3.02 cm^2) was recorded in control. During the second year (2009-10) of experimentation, maximum unit leaf area (4.84 cm^2) was recorded with the application of 0.5% zinc sulphate in combination with 0.6% boric acid. The treatments comprising foliar application of 0.5% zinc sulphate in combination with 0.5% boric acid, 0.6% zinc sulphate in combination with 0.5% boric acid, 0.6% zinc sulphate in combination with 0.6% boric acid, 0.4% zinc sulphate in combination with 0.6% boric acid, 0.6% zinc sulphate in combination with 0.4% boric acid and 0.4% zinc sulphate in combination with 0.5% boric acid were equally effective in improving the unit leaf area registering values of 4.72, 4.51, 4.50, 4.37, 4.36 and 4.34 cm^2, respectively whereas, minimum unit leaf area (3.13 cm^2) was observed in untreated trees. The pooled data showed that maximum unit leaf area of 4.82 cm^2 was obtained with the foliar application of 0.5% zinc sulphate in combination with 0.6% boric acid and was at par with the values observed with the foliar application of 0.5% zinc sulphate in combination with 0.5% boric acid (4.66 cm^2), 0.6% zinc sulphate in combination with 0.4% boric acid (4.52 cm^2), 0.6% zinc sulphate in combination with 0.6% boric acid (4.49 cm^2) and 0.6% zinc sulphate in combination with 0.5% boric acid (4.36 cm^2) whereas, unit leaf area (3.08 cm^2) was minimum in control.

4.1.2.3 Specific leaf area

The data pertaining to effect of girdling as well as foliar spraying of zinc and boron applied singly or in combination with each other on specific leaf area is presented in Table 3. Perusal of the data revealed that during 2008-09 maximum specific leaf area (8.24 cm^2 g^{-1}) was recorded in trees sprayed with 0.6% zinc sulphate in combination with 0.5% boric acid closely followed by application of 0.6% zinc sulphate in combination with 0.4% boric acid, 0.5% zinc sulphate in combination with 0.6% boric acid, 0.5% zinc sulphate in combination with 0.4% boric acid, 0.6% zinc sulphate in combination with 0.6% boric acid, 0.4% zinc sulphate in combination with 0.5% boric acid, 0.6% boric acid alone, 0.5% zinc sulphate in combination with 0.5% boric acid and 0.5% boric acid applied alone registering values of 8.09, 7.83, 7.76, 7.47, 7.20, 7.07, 6.98 and 6.06 cm^2 g^{-1}, respectively which were at par with each other whereas, minimum specific leaf area (4.23 cm^2 g^{-1}) was recorded in girdled trees of olive. In second year of experimentation (2009-10) specific leaf area ranged from 3.65 to 7.92 with a maximum value of 7.92 cm^2 g^{-1} in trees sprayed with 0.4% zinc sulphate in combination with 0.6% boric acid whereas, minimum value (3.65 cm^2 g^{-1}) was recorded in untreated trees of olive. It is clear from the pooled data that maximum specific leaf area (7.78 cm^2 g^{-1}) was observed with foliar application of 0.6% zinc sulphate in combination with 0.4% boric acid closely followed by foliar application of 0.6% zinc sulphate in combination with 0.5% boric acid, 0.5% zinc sulphate in combination with 0.6% boric acid, 0.5% zinc sulphate in combination with 0.5% boric acid, 0.6% zinc sulphate in combination with 0.6% boric acid and 0.5% zinc sulphate in combination with 0.4% boric acid registering 7.67, 7.34, 7.27, 7.11 and 7.10 cm^2 g^{-1} specific leaf area respectively and were at par with each other whereas, minimum specific leaf area (4.07 cm^2 g^{-1}) was observed in control.

4.1.3 Leaf water content, stomatal count and chlorophyll content

The data pertaining to effect of girdling as well as foliar application of zinc and boron applied singly or in combination with each other on leaf water content, stomatal count and chlorophyll content is embodied in the Table 4.

4.1.3.1 Leaf water content

Perusal of the data revealed that leaf water content of olive was significantly influenced by different micro-nutrient sprays during 2008-09 as well as during 2009-10. The application of 0.6% zinc sulphate in combination with 0.4% boric acid in olive trees resulted in highest leaf water content of 59.00 per cent during the first year of experimentation closely followed by the trees sprayed with 0.5% zinc sulphate in combination with 0.6% boric acid, 0.6% zinc sulphate in combination with 0.6% boric acid, 0.6% zinc sulphate in combination with 0.5% boric acid, 0.5% zinc sulphate in combination with 0.5% boric acid and 0.5% zinc sulphate in combination with 0.4% boric acid registering values of 58.77, 58.77, 58.48, 56.82 and 56.67 percent, respectively which were at par with each other, while minimum (44.10%) the leaf water content was recorded in control.

Table 4: Effect of girdling, zinc and boron on leaf water content, stomatal count, and chlorophyll content of olive cv. Frontoio.

Treatment	Leaf water content (%)			Stomatal count (Number/ microscopic field)			Chlorophyll content (mg/g)		
	2008-09	2009-10	Pooled	2008-09	2009-10	Pooled	2008-09	2009-10	Pooled
T_1	44.10	43.03	43.57	20.58	21.33	20.96	1.10	1.02	1.06
T_2	45.90	43.53	44.72	21.58	22.50	22.04	1.17	1.11	1.14
T_3	48.39	44.74	46.57	20.92	21.50	21.21	1.25	1.18	1.21
T_4	49.53	45.98	47.75	21.92	22.67	22.29	1.36	1.30	1.33
T_5	50.73	46.98	48.86	22.25	22.83	22.54	1.42	1.37	1.40
T_6	51.99	48.36	50.18	21.92	22.33	22.13	1.21	1.16	1.18
T_7	52.83	48.89	50.86	23.00	23.42	23.21	1.32	1.27	1.29
T_8	53.15	49.05	51.10	23.25	23.75	23.50	1.40	1.35	1.38
T_9	53.40	51.00	51.80	22.25	22.83	22.54	1.28	1.21	1.24
T_{10}	54.60	51.48	53.04	22.92	23.50	23.21	1.44	1.31	1.38
T_{11}	55.50	51.96	53.73	23.25	23.67	23.46	1.53	1.47	1.50
T_{12}	56.67	52.91	54.79	22.58	23.08	22.83	1.35	1.30	1.32
T_{13}	56.82	53.93	55.38	24.00	24.67	24.33	1.48	1.42	1.45
T_{14}	58.77	54.42	56.59	24.33	24.75	24.54	1.51	1.45	1.48
T_{15}	59.00	54.56	56.78	23.42	24.08	23.75	1.31	1.25	1.28
T_{16}	58.48	54.32	56.40	24.00	24.42	24.21	1.38	1.32	1.35
T_{17}	58.77	54.43	56.60	23.75	24.50	24.13	1.43	1.38	1.40
$C.D_{(0.05)}$	3.48	3.32	2.36	2.12	2.10	1.47	0.11	0.13	0.08

In the second year of study (2009-10), trees sprayed with 0.6% zinc sulphate in combination with 0.4% boric acid resulted in highest leaf water content of 54.56 per cent closely followed by trees sprayed with 0.6% zinc sulphate in combination with 0.6% boric acid, 0.5% zinc sulphate in combination with 0.6% boric acid, 0.6% zinc sulphate in combination with 0.5% boric acid, 0.5% zinc sulphate in combination with 0.5% boric acid, 0.5% zinc sulphate in combination with 0.4% boric acid, 0.4% zinc sulphate in combination with 0.6% boric acid and 0.4% zinc sulphate in combination with 0.5% boric acid registering leaf water content of 54.43, 54.42, 54.32, 53.93, 52.91, 51.96 and 51.48 percent, respectively and were at par with each other. Lowest leaf water content of 43.03 percent was recorded in untreated trees. In the pooled data highest leaf water content (56.78%) was observed in trees sprayed with 0.6% zinc sulphate and 0.4% boric acid, closely followed by 0.6% zinc sulphate in combination with 0.6% boric acid, 0.5% zinc sulphate in combination with 0.6% boric acid, 0.6% zinc sulphate in combination with 0.5% boric acid, 0.5% zinc sulphate in combination with 0.5% boric acid and 0.5% zinc sulphate in combination with 0.4% boric acid with respective values of 56.60, 56.59, 56.40, 55.38 and 54.79 percent and were at par with each other. Lowest leaf water content (43.57%) was obtained in untreated trees and was par with leaf water content found in girdled trees (44.72%).

4.1.3.2 Stomatal count

The stomatal count was significantly influenced different treatments during both the years of investigation. The olive trees receiving spray of 0.5% zinc sulphate in combination with 0.6% boric acid exhibited highest stomatal count of 24.33 number/ microscopic field in the first year of experimentation, whereas the lowest stomatal count of 20.58 number/ microscopic field was recorded in untreated trees. During second year, the stomatal count ranged from 21.33 to 24.75 number/microscopic field with all the treatments tried in this study wherein highest stomatal count (24.75 number/microscopic field) was recorded in trees sprayed with 0.5% zinc sulphate in combination with 0.6% boric acid and least stomatal count (21.33 number/ microscopic field) was observed in untreated trees. The perusal of the pooled data showed that the highest stomatal count (24.54 number/microscopic field) was found in trees sprayed with 0.5% zinc sulphate in combination with 0.6% boric acid whereas, stomatal count was minimum (20.96 number/microscopic field) in untreated trees.

4.1.3.3 Chlorophyll content

An inquisition of the data showed that during 2008-09 highest leaf chlorophyll content (1.53mg/g) was estimated in trees sprayed with 0.4% zinc sulphate in combination with 0.6% boric acid closely followed by trees sprayed with 0.5% zinc sulphate in combination with 0.6% boric acid, 0.5% zinc sulphate in combination with 0.5% boric acid, 0.4% zinc sulphate in combination with 0.5% boric acid and 0.6% zinc sulphate in combination with 0.6% boric acid registering values of 1.51, 1.48, 1.44 and 1.43 mg/g, respectively which were at par with each other, whereas lowest leaf chlorophyll content (1.10 mg/g) was obtained in untreated trees which was at par with chlorophyll content recorded in girdled trees (1.17 mg/g). The results of second year trial also exhibited similar pattern as was observed in the first year of study. The leaf chlorophyll content ranged from 1.02 to 1.47 mg/g registering highest chlorophyll content (1.47 mg/g) in trees sprayed with 0.4% zinc sulphate in combination with 0.6% boric acid and lowest leaf chlorophyll content (1.02 mg/g) in untreated trees. The pooled data pertaining to leaf chlorophyll content showed that highest leaf chlorophyll content of 1.50 mg/g was observed in the trees sprayed with 0.4% zinc sulphate in combination with 0.6% boric acid and was at par with the values found in trees sprayed with 0.5% zinc sulphate in combination with 0.6% boric acid (1.48 mg/g) and 0.5% zinc sulphate in combination with 0.5% boric acid (1.45 mg/g). The lowest leaf chlorophyll content (1.06 mg/g) was found in control.

4.1.4 Flowering characteristics

The data on duration of flowering, blooming intensity and proportion of perfect flowers is presented in Table 5 and depicted in fig. 1 and plate 2.

4.1.4.1 Duration of flowering

Duration of flowering was not significantly influenced by different treatments during 2008-09 and spray of 0.6% zinc sulphate in combination with 0.4% boric acid shortened the duration of flowering by 2.66 days from 19.33 days in untreated trees. During second year of experimentation, minimum duration of flowering (15.67 days) was observed in trees sprayed with 0.6% zinc sulphate in combination with 0.6% boric acid and was significantly higher than the duration of flowering recorded in all the treatments tried. However, maximum duration of flowering (19.00 days) was observed in untreated trees. The pooled data showed that different treatments

Table 5: Effect of girdling, zinc and boron on duration of flowering, blooming intensity, and proportion of perfect flowers of olive cv. Frontoio.

Treatment	Duration of flowering (days)			Blooming Intensity(%)			Proportion of perfect flowers (%)		
	2008-09	2009-10	Pooled	2008-09	2009-10	Pooled	2008-09	2009-10	Pooled
T_1	19.33 (4.51)	19.00 (4.47)	19.17 (4.49)	0.42 (1.19)	0.31 (1.15)	0.37 (1.17)	30.67	26.67	28.67
T_2	17.00 (4.24)	17.67 (4.32)	17.33 (4.28)	0.48 (1.22)	0.38 (1.18)	0.43 (1.20)	36.00	33.33	34.67
T_3	18.67 (4.43)	18.33 (4.40)	18.50 (4.42)	0.45 (1.21)	0.35 (1.16)	0.40 (1.18)	37.33	33.33	35.33
T_4	18.33 (4.40)	17.00 (4.24)	17.67 (4.32)	0.49 (1.22)	0.38 (1.18)	0.44 (1.20)	38.67	37.33	38.00
T_5	17.67 (4.32)	17.33 (4.28)	17.50 (4.30)	0.50 (1.22)	0.40 (1.18)	0.45 (1.20)	40.00	36.00	38.00
T_6	17.00 (4.24)	17.33 (4.28)	17.17 (4.26)	0.47 (1.21)	0.37 (1.17)	0.42 (1.19)	41.33	37.33	39.33
T_7	17.33 (4.28)	17.33 (4.28)	17.33 (4.28)	0.50 (1.22)	0.42 (1.19)	0.46 (1.21)	45.33	37.33	41.33
T_8	16.67 (4.20)	17.00 (4.24)	16.83 (4.22)	0.52 (1.23)	0.41 (1.19)	0.46 (1.21)	44.00	40.00	42.00
T_9	17.67 (4.32)	18.33 (4.40)	18.00 (4.36)	0.52 (1.23)	0.43 (1.19)	0.47 (1.21)	41.33	41.33	41.33
T_{10}	17.67 (4.32)	18.00 (4.36)	17.83 (4.34)	0.54 (1.24)	0.43 (1.20)	0.49 (1.22)	48.00	46.67	47.33
T_{11}	18.00 (4.36)	17.33 (4.28)	17.67 (4.32)	0.54 (1.24)	0.44 (1.20)	0.49 (1.22)	46.67	44.00	45.33
T_{12}	18.00 (4.36)	17.67 (4.32)	17.83 (4.34)	0.54 (1.24)	0.45 (1.20)	0.50 (1.22)	45.33	41.33	43.33
T_{13}	17.33 (4.28)	17.33 (4.28)	17.33 (4.28)	0.56 (1.25)	0.45 (1.20)	0.50 (1.22)	49.33	45.33	47.33
T_{14}	17.33 (4.28)	17.67 (4.32)	17.50 (4.30)	0.56 (1.25)	0.44 (1.20)	0.50 (1.22)	48.00	44.00	46.00
T_{15}	16.67 (4.20)	16.67 (4.20)	16.67 (4.20)	0.54 (1.24)	0.44 (1.20)	0.49 (1.22)	45.33	41.33	43.33
T_{16}	17.00 (4.24)	16.67 (4.20)	16.83 (4.22)	0.55 (1.25)	0.45 (1.20)	0.50 (1.22)	49.33	46.67	48.00
T_{17}	18.00 (4.36)	15.67 (4.08)	16.83 (4.22)	0.56 (1.25)	0.45 (1.20)	0.50 (1.22)	45.33	42.67	44.00
C.D$_{(0.05)}$	NS	0.16	0.12	0.01	0.01	0.009	7.24	7.14	4.99

Figures within the parentheses are transformed means

significantly influenced the duration of flowering. The duration of flowering was reduced by 2.34 days from 19.17 days in untreated trees to 16.83 days in trees sprayed with 0.6% zinc sulphate in combination with 0.5% boric acid and 0.6% zinc sulphate in combination with 0.6% boric acid.

Plate 2: Flowering in olive trees sprayed with 0.5% zinc sulphate in combination with 0.5% boric acid.

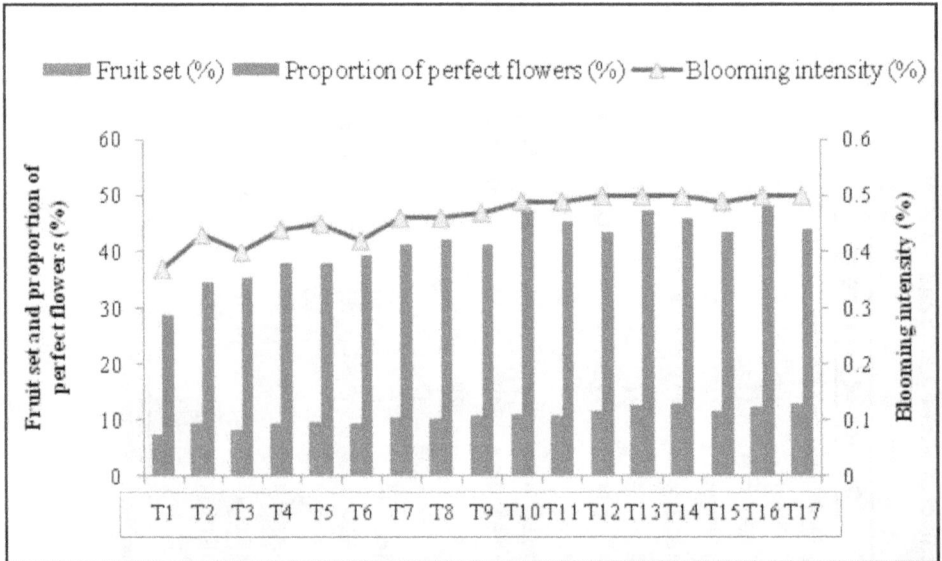

Fig 1: Effect of girdling, zinc and boron on blooming intensity, proportion of perfect flowers and fruit set of olive cv. Frontoio (Pooled data)

4.1.4.2 Blooming intensity

During 2008-09, highest blooming intensity of 0.56 per cent was recorded in trees sprayed with 0.5% zinc sulphate in combination with 0.5% boric acid, 0.5% zinc sulphate in combination with 0.6% boric acid and 0.6% zinc sulphate in combination with 0.6% boric acid, whereas lowest blooming intensity of 0.42 per cent was observed in untreated trees. In the second year (2009-10) of experimentation, highest blooming intensity of 0.45 percent was found in trees sprayed with 0.6% zinc sulphate in combination with 0.6% boric acid, 0.6% zinc sulphate in combination with 0.5% boric acid, 0.5% zinc sulphate in combination with 0.5% boric acid, 0.5% zinc sulphate in combination with 0.4% boric acid whereas, lowest blooming intensity (0.31%) in untreated trees. The pooled data showed that blooming intensity was significantly influenced by different treatments, exhibiting highest blooming intensity of 0.50 per cent in trees sprayed with 0.5% zinc sulphate in combination with 0.4% boric acid, 0.5% zinc sulphate in combination with 0.5% boric acid, 0.5% zinc sulphate in combination with 0.6% boric acid, 0.6% zinc sulphate in combination with 0.5% boric acid and 0.6% zinc sulphate in combination with 0.6% boric acid whereas, lowest blooming intensity of 0.37% was obtained in untreated trees.

4.1.4.3 Proportion of perfect flowers

Different treatments significantly improved the proportion of perfect flower over control during 2008-09 as well as in 2009-10. The proportion of perfect flowers reached to a maximum of 49.33 per cent in trees sprayed with 0.6% zinc sulphate in combination with 0.5% boric acid and 0.5% zinc sulphate in combination with 0.5% boric acid during 2008-09. The lowest proportion of perfect flowers (30.67%) was observed in untreated trees. During 2009-10, the proportion of perfect flowers ranged from 26.67 to 46.67 percent with all the treatments tried under this study wherein highest proportion of perfect flowers (46.67%) was recorded in treatments with 0.6% zinc sulphate in combination with 0.5% boric acid and 0.4% zinc sulphate in combination with 0.5% boric acid closely followed by 0.5% zinc sulphate in combination with 0.5% boric acid, 0.5% zinc sulphate in combination with 0.6% boric acid, 0.4% zinc sulphate in combination with 0.6% boric acid and 0.6% zinc sulphate in combination with 0.6% boric acid registering 45.33, 44.00, 44.00, 42.67 percent proportion of perfect flowers, respectively and were at par with each other. The pooled data showed that girdling and spray of zinc and boron singly or in combination with each other significantly improved the proportion of perfect flowers as compared to control trees. The highest percentage of perfect flowers (48.00%) was observed in trees sprayed with 0.6% zinc sulphate in combination with 0.5% boric acid which was at par with the proportion of perfect flowers found in trees sprayed with 0.5% zinc sulphate in combination with 0.5% boric acid and 0.4% zinc sulphate in combination with 0.5% boric acid (47.33%), 0.5% zinc sulphate in combination with 0.6% boric acid (46.00%), 0.4% zinc sulphate in combination with 0.6% boric acid (45.33%), 0.5% zinc sulphate in combination with 0.4% boric acid (43.33%) and 0.6% zinc sulphate in combination with 0.4% boric acid (43.33%). However, lowest proportion of perfect flowers (28.67%) was observed in untreated trees.

4.1.5 Fruiting characteristics

The data regarding the effect of girdling, zinc and boron applied singly or in combination with each other on fruit set, fruit drop and fruit yield is embodied in Table 6 and depicted in fig. 2 and plate 3.

Table 6: Effect of girdling, zinc and boron on fruit set, fruit drop and fruit yield of olive cv. Frontoio.

Treatment	Fruit set (%)			Fruit drop (%)			Fruit yield (Kg tree⁻¹)		
	2008-09	2009-10	Pooled	2008-09	2009-10	Pooled	2008-09	2009-10	Pooled
T_1	9.85	5.30	7.57	62.06	62.18	62.12	1.94	1.03	1.48
	(3.29)	(2.51)	(2.90)						
T_2	12.52	6.43	9.48	58.8	57.39	58.09	2.19	1.14	1.66
	(3.67)	(2.72)	(3.19)						
T_3	11.17	5.55	8.36	60.39	60.38	60.38	2.12	1.04	1.58
	(3.48)	(2.56)	(3.02)						
T_4	12.25	6.44	9.34 x	58.93	60.26	59.59	2.18	1.08	1.63
	(3.63)	(2.72)	(2.72)						
T_5	12.77	6.67	9.72	58.15	58.82	58.49	2.24	1.11	1.67
	(3.71)	(2.77)	(3.24)						
T_6	12.10	6.93	9.52	58.8	58.09	58.45	2.25	1.11	1.68
	(3.62)	(2.80)	(3.21)						
T_7	13.37	7.51	10.44	57.47	56.51	56.99	2.31	1.15	1.73
	(3.79)	(2.90)	(3.35)						
T_8	13.27	7.15	10.21	57.6	56.83	57.21	2.37	1.18	1.77
	(3.77)	(2.84)	(3.31)						
T_9	13.04	8.26	10.65	58.2	57.19	57.7	2.36	1.17	1.77
	(3.74)	(3.04)	(3.39)						
T_{10}	13.58	8.48	11.03	55.88	54.62	55.25	2.41	1.19	1.8
	(3.82)	(3.08)	(3.45)						
T_{11}	13.80	7.86	10.83	56.5	55.74	56.12	2.39	1.19	1.79
	(3.84)	(2.97)	(3.41)						
T_{12}	14.97	8.21	11.59	56.8	53.2	55	2.44	1.21	1.82
	(3.99)	(3.03)	(3.51)						
T_{13}	15.97	9.70	12.84	52.71	51.7	52.21	2.56	1.28	1.92
	(4.12)	(3.27)	(3.69)						
T_{14}	16.37	9.78	13.08	54.37	53.35	53.86	2.44	1.21	1.83
	(4.17)	(3.28)	(3.73)						
T_{15}	15.19	7.96	11.59	55.25	55.91	55.58	2.45	1.21	1.83
	(4.02)	(2.99)	(3.50)						
T_{16}	15.83	9.29	12.56	53.1	53.92	53.51	2.53	1.26	1.89
	(4.10)	(3.21)	(3.65)						
T_{17}	16.41	9.50	12.95	54.23	51.96	53.09	2.46	1.23	1.84
	(4.17)	(3.24)	(3.70)						
$C.D_{(0.05)}$	0.34	0.31	0.23	3.48	6.12	3.46	0.14	0.07	0.08

Figures within the parentheses are transformed means.

4.1.5.1 Fruit set

Fruit set was significantly influenced by different treatments during both the years of investigation. During 2008-09, highest fruit set (16.41%) was recorded in trees sprayed with 0.6% zinc sulphate in combination with 0.6% boric acid which was at par with fruit set recorded in trees sprayed with 0.5% zinc sulphate in combination with 0.6% boric acid (16.37%) whereas, minimum fruit set (9.85%) was observed in untreated trees. In the second year of investigation, the fruit set was low as compared to the fruit set during the first year of investigations. The highest fruit set of 9.78 percent was recorded in the trees sprayed with 0.5% zinc sulphate in combination with 0.6% boric acid closely followed by the trees sprayed with 0.5% zinc sulphate in combination with 0.5% boric acid and 0.6% zinc sulphate in combination with 0.6% boric acid registering fruit set of 9.70 and 9.50 percent, respectively and were at par with each other. The lowest fruit set of 5.30 per cent was recorded in untreated trees which was at par with fruit set recorded in trees sprayed with 0.4% zinc sulphate alone. The pooled data showed significant influence of different treatments on fruit set. Maximum fruit set (13.08%) was observed in trees sprayed with 0.5% zinc sulphate in combination with 0.6% boric acid closely followed by trees sprayed with 0.6% zinc sulphate in combination with 0.6% boric acid and 0.5% zinc sulphate in combination with 0.5% boric acid having a fruit set of 12.95 and 12.84 percent, respectively which were at par with each other. However, minimum fruit set (7.57%) was obtained in untreated trees.

Plate 3: Fruiting in olive trees sprayed with 0.5% zinc sulphate in combination with 0.5% boric acid

4.1.5.2 Fruit drop

During 2008-09, minimum fruit drop of 52.71 per cent was recorded in trees sprayed with 0.5% zinc sulphate in combination with 0.5% boric acid which was at par with fruit drop recorded in trees sprayed with 0.6% zinc sulphate in combination with 0.5% boric acid, 0.6% zinc sulphate in combination with 0.6% boric acid, 0.5% zinc sulphate in combination with 0.6% boric acid, 0.6% zinc sulphate in combination with 0.4% boric acid and 0.4% zinc sulphate in combination with 0.5% boric acid exhibiting respective values of 53.10, 54.23, 54.37, 55.25, 55.88 percent, whereas, maximum fruit drop (62.06%) was recorded in untreated trees. During the second year of investigation, fruit drop ranged from 51.70 to 62.18 percent with all the treatments tried in this study, wherein lowest fruit drop (51.70%) was recorded in trees sprayed with 0.5% zinc sulphate in combination with 0.5% boric acid and highest fruit drop (62.18%) was found in untreated trees. The pooled data showed that girdling as well as micro-nutrient sprays significantly reduced fruit drop as compared to control. Minimum fruit drop (52.21%) was observed in trees sprayed with 0.5% zinc sulphate in combination with 0.5% boric acid closely followed by trees sprayed with 0.6% Zinc sulphate in combination with 0.6% boric acid, 0.6% zinc sulphate in combination with 0.5% boric acid, 0.5% zinc sulphate in combination with 0.6% boric acid, 0.5% zinc sulphate in combination with 0.4% boric acid, 0.4% zinc sulphate in combination with 0.5% boric acid, 0.6% zinc sulphate in combination with 0.4% boric acid and 0.4% zinc sulphate in combination with 0.6% boric acid registering 53.09%, 53.51%, 53.86%, 55.00%, 55.25%, 55.58% and 56.12% fruit drop, respectively and were at par with each other. The maximum fruit drop (62.12%) was observed in untreated trees.

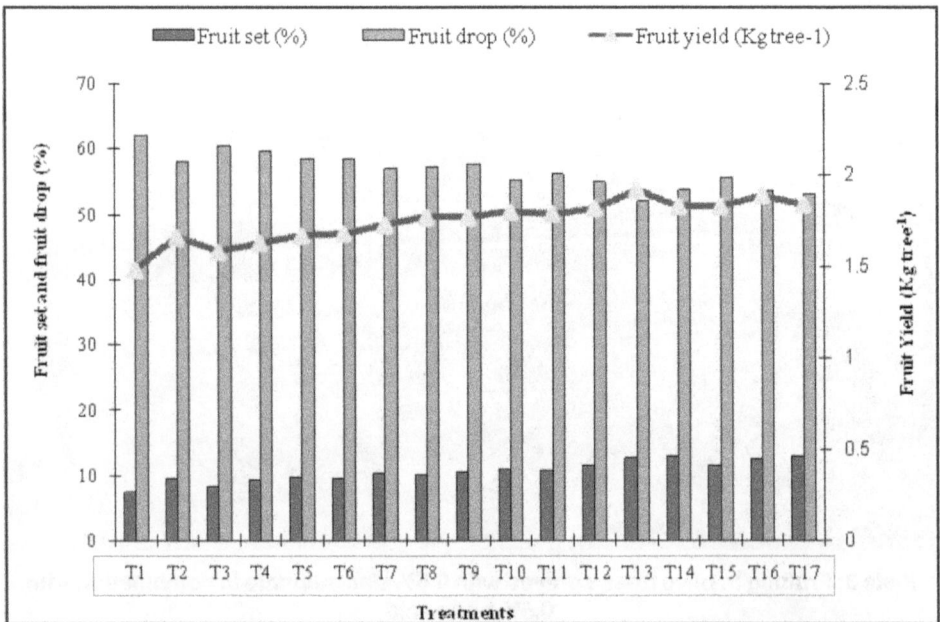

Fig. 2: Effect of girdling, zinc and boron on fruit set, fruit drop and fruit yield of olive cv. Frontoio (Pooled Data)

4.1.5.3 Fruit yield

Fruit yield was significantly affected by different treatments and it ranged from 1.94 to 2.56 kg tree^{-1} during 2008-09. Foliar application of 0.5% zinc sulphate in combination with 0.5% boric acid resulted in highest fruit yield of 2.56 Kg tree^{-1} whereas, lowest fruit yield of 1.94 Kg tree^{-1} was obtained from untreated trees. The results of second year showed highest fruit yield of 1.28 Kg tree^{-1} in trees sprayed with 0.5% zinc sulphate in combination with 0.5% boric acid closely followed by trees sprayed with 0.6% zinc sulphate in combination with 0.5% boric acid and 0.6% zinc sulphate in combination with 0.6% boric acid registering a fruit yield of 1.26 and 1.23 Kg tree^{-1}, respectively and were at par with each other whereas, lowest fruit yield of 1.03 Kg tree^{-1} was observed in untreated trees. But an overall decrease in yield was recorded in all the treatments tried as compared to fruit yield obtained in the first year. An inquisition of the pooled data showed that highest fruit yield (1.92 Kg tree^{-1}) was observed in trees sprayed with 0.5% zinc sulphate in combination with 0.5% boric acid closely followed by trees sprayed with 0.6% zinc sulphate in combination with 0.5% boric acid and 0.6% zinc sulphate in combination with 0.6% boric acid registering a fruit yield of 1.89 and 1.84 Kg tree^{-1} and were at par with each other. The lowest fruit yield of 1.48 Kg tree^{-1} was found in untreated trees.

4.1.6 Physical parameters of fruits

The data pertaining to effect of girdling, zinc and boron applied singly or in combination with each other on fruit size, fruit weight and fruit volume of olive cultivar Frontoio has been presented in Table 7.

Table 7: Effect of girdling, zinc and boron on fruit size, fruit weight and fruit volume of olive cv. Frontoio.

Treatment	Fruit size(cm)			Fruit weight(g)			Fruit volume(cc)		
	2008-09	2009-10	Pooled	2008-09	2009-10	Pooled	2008-09	2009-10	Pooled
T_1	1.27	1.29	1.28	1.13	1.18	1.15	1.31	1.33	1.32
T_2	1.34	1.37	1.35	1.21	1.26	1.24	1.39	1.41	1.40
T_3	1.31	1.33	1.32	1.16	1.22	1.19	1.35	1.37	1.36
T_4	1.34	1.36	1.35	1.20	1.24	1.22	1.38	1.40	1.39
T_5	1.35	1.39	1.37	1.22	1.27	1.24	1.40	1.41	1.41
T_6	1.36	1.38	1.37	1.21	1.28	1.24	1.40	1.42	1.41
T_7	1.43	1.40	1.42	1.27	1.30	1.28	1.44	1.46	1.45
T_8	1.45	1.41	1.43	1.29	1.33	1.31	1.44	1.47	1.46
T_9	1.44	1.44	1.44	1.27	1.36	1.32	1.46	1.49	1.48
T_{10}	1.51	1.46	1.49	1.32	1.38	1.35	1.50	1.53	1.51
T_{11}	1.55	1.43	1.49	1.34	1.41	1.38	1.49	1.54	1.52
T_{12}	1.52	1.52	1.52	1.32	1.45	1.39	1.51	1.55	1.53
T_{13}	1.60	1.54	1.57	1.39	1.50	1.45	1.59	1.63	1.61
T_{14}	1.62	1.51	1.56	1.41	1.51	1.46	1.53	1.64	1.58
T_{15}	1.56	1.54	1.55	1.35	1.48	1.42	1.55	1.59	1.57
T_{16}	1.60	1.56	1.58	1.38	1.49	1.44	1.58	1.63	1.61
T_{17}	1.62	1.57	1.59	1.39	1.51	1.45	1.59	1.62	1.60
C.D $_{(0.05)}$	0.09	0.08	0.06	0.07	0.03	0.04	0.08	0.05	0.05

4.1.6.1 Fruit size

The perusal of the data showed that fruit size was significantly affected by different treatments during both the years of investigation. The application of 0.5% zinc sulphate in combination with 0.6% boric acid and 0.6% zinc sulphate in combination with 0.6% boric acid recorded maximum fruit size of 1.62 cm during the first year of experimentation closely followed by trees sprayed with 0.6% zinc sulphate in combination with 0.5% boric acid and 0.5% zinc sulphate in combination with 0.5% boric acid, 0.6% zinc sulphate in combination with 0.4% boric acid, 0.4% zinc sulphate in combination with 0.6% boric acid registering fruit size of 1.60 cm, 1.60 cm, 1.56 cm and 1.55 cm, respectively and were at par with each other. Minimum fruit size (1.27 cm) was recorded in untreated trees. However, during the second year (2009-10) of experimentation, fruit size ranged from 1.29 cm to 1.57 cm with all the treatments tried in this study wherein, maximum fruit size (1.57 cm) was obtained in trees sprayed with 0.6% zinc sulphate in combination with 0.6% boric acid and minimum fruit size (1.29 cm) was recorded in untreated trees. The pooled data revealed that maximum fruit size (1.59 cm) was found in trees sprayed with 0.6% zinc sulphate in combination with 0.6% boric acid, closely followed by trees sprayed with 0.6% zinc sulphate in combination with 0.5% boric acid, 0.5% zinc sulphate in combination with 0.5% boric acid, 0.5% zinc sulphate in combination with 0.6% boric acid, and 0.6% zinc sulphate in combination with 0.4% boric acid registering fruit size 1.58, 1.57, 1.56 and 1.55 cm, respectively. Minimum fruit size (1.28 cm) was obtained in untreated trees and was at par with fruit size observed in trees sprayed with 0.4% zinc sulphate (1.32 cm).

4.1.6.2 Fruit weight

Maximum fruit weight of 1.41 g was recorded in trees sprayed with 0.5% zinc sulphate in combination with 0.6% boric acid closely followed by trees sprayed with 0.6% zinc sulphate in combination with 0.6% boric acid and 0.5% zinc sulphate in combination with 0.5% boric acid, 0.6% zinc sulphate in combination with 0.5% boric acid, 0.6% zinc sulphate in combination with 0.4% boric acid and 0.4% zinc sulphate in combination with 0.6% boric acid showing fruit size of 1.39, 1.39, 1.38, 1.35 and 1.34 g, respectively and were at par with each other. Minimum fruit weight of 1.13 g was recorded in untreated trees. During the second year of investigation, fruit weight ranged from 1.18 g to 1.51 g wherein, maximum fruit weight (1.51 g) was recorded in trees sprayed with 0.6% zinc sulphate in combination with 0.6% boric acid and 0.5% zinc sulphate in combination with 0.6% boric acid and minimum fruit (1.18 g) in untreated trees. From the pooled data it is evident that maximum fruit weight (1.46 g) was found in trees sprayed with 0.5% zinc sulphate in combination with 0.6% boric acid which was at par with trees sprayed with 0.6% zinc sulphate in combination with 0.6% boric acid (1.45 g), 0.5% zinc sulphate in combination with 0.5% boric acid (1.45 g), 0.6% zinc sulphate in combination with 0.5% boric acid (1.44 g), and 0.6% Zinc sulphate in combination with 0.4% boric acid (1.42 g). Minimum fruit weight (1.15 g) was observed in untreated trees.

4.1.6.3 Fruit volume

Highest fruit volume (1.59 cc) was recorded in trees sprayed with 0.6% zinc sulphate in combination with 0.6% boric acid and 0.5% zinc sulphate in combination with 0.5% boric acid during 2008-09, closely followed by application of 0.6% zinc sulphate in combination with 0.5% boric acid, 0.6% zinc sulphate in combination with 0.4% boric acid, 0.5% zinc sulphate in combination with 0.6% boric acid and 0.5% zinc sulphate in combination with 0.4% boric acid registering fruit volume of 1.58 cc, 1.55 cc, 1.53 cc and 1.51 cc, respectively and were at par with each other. The data for the second year of study (2009-10) showed that the fruit volume ranged from 1.33 cc to 1.64 cc wherein, highest fruit volume (1.64 cc) was recorded in trees sprayed with 0.5% zinc sulphate in combination with 0.6% boric acid closely followed by fruit volume of 1.63 cc in trees sprayed with 0.6% zinc sulphate in combination with 0.5% boric acid and with 0.5% zinc sulphate in combination with 0.5% boric acid, 1.62 cc with 0.6% zinc sulphate in combination with 0.6% boric acid and 1.59cc with 0.6% zinc sulphate in combination with 0.4% boric acid whereas lowest fruit volume (1.33 cc) was recorded in untreated trees of olive. It is evident from the pooled data that highest fruit volume (1.61cc) was found in trees sprayed with 0.5% zinc sulphate in combination with 0.5% boric acid and 0.6% zinc sulphate in combination with 0.5% boric acid closely followed by trees sprayed with 0.6% zinc sulphate in combination with 0.6% boric acid, 0.5% zinc sulphate in combination with 0.6% boric acid, and 0.6% zinc sulphate in combination with 0.4% boric acid registering fruit volume of 1.60 cc, 1.58 cc and 1.57 cc, respectively and were at par with each other whereas lowest fruit volume of 1.32 cc was observed in untreated trees closely followed by trees sprayed with 0.4% zinc sulphate (1.36 cc) alone and were at par with each other.

4.1.7 Pulp: stone ratio and oil content

The data regarding above mentioned parameters is presented in the Table 8 and depicted in fig. 3.

4.1.7.1 Pulp: stone ratio

In the first year of study, pulp: stone ratio reached to a maximum of 2.53 in trees sprayed with 0.6% zinc sulphate in combination with 0.6% boric acid closely followed by trees sprayed with 0.6% zinc sulphate in combination with 0.5% boric acid, 0.5% zinc sulphate in combination with 0.5% boric acid and 0.6% zinc sulphate in combination with 0.4% boric acid registering values of 2.51, 2.49 and 2.48, respectively and were at par with each other. However, minimum pulp: stone ratio of 2.21 was obtained in untreated trees and was statistically at par with pulp: stone ratio recorded in trees sprayed with 0.4% zinc sulphate alone. The pulp: stone ratio during the second year of experimentation (2009-10) ranged from 2.28 to 2.62 wherein, maximum pulp: stone ratio (2.62) was recorded in trees sprayed with 0.6% zinc sulphate in combination with 0.5% boric acid and minimum pulp: stone ratio (2.28) was obtained under untreated trees. The pooled data showed that maximum pulp: stone ratio (2.57) was observed in trees sprayed with 0.6% zinc sulphate in combination with 0.6% boric acid closely followed by trees sprayed with 0.6% zinc sulphate in combination with 0.5% boric acid, 0.5% zinc sulphate in combination with 0.5% boric acid, 0.6% zinc sulphate in combination with 0.4% boric acid, 0.5% zinc sulphate in combination with 0.6% boric acid, and 0.5% zinc sulphate in combination with 0.4% boric acid registering pulp: stone ratio of 2.56, 2.55, 2.53, 2.50 and 2.50, respectively and were at par with each other. The minimum pulp: stone ratio (2.24) was found in untreated trees.

Table 8: Effect of girdling, zinc and boron on pulp: stone ratio and oil content of olive cv. Frontoio.

Treatment	Pulp: stone ratio			Oil content (%)		
	2008-09	2009-10	Pooled	2008-09	2009-10	Pooled
T_1	2.21	2.28	2.24	21.23 (4.72)	20.68 (4.66)	20.96 (4.69)
T_2	2.28	2.36	2.32	22.20 (4.82)	22.03 (4.80)	22.12 (4.81)
T_3	2.25	2.66	2.45	21.86 (4.78)	21.84 (4.78)	21.85 (4.78)
T_4	2.28	2.36	2.32	22.28 (4.82)	22.57 (4.85)	22.42 (4.84)
T_5	2.30	2.38	2.34	22.62 (4.86)	22.92 (4.89)	22.77 (4.88)
T_6	2.30	2.39	2.34	23.11 (4.91)	23.41 (4.94)	23.26 (4.93)
T_7	2.33	2.42	2.37	23.10 (4.91)	23.40 (4.94)	23.25 (4.92)
T_8	2.35	2.43	2.39	23.19 (4.92)	23.49 (4.95)	23.34 (4.93)
T_9	2.36	2.46	2.41	24.02 (5.00)	24.30 (5.03)	24.16 (5.02)
T_{10}	2.39	2.50	2.44	24.01 (5.00)	24.28 (5.03)	24.15 (5.01)
T_{11}	2.39	2.50	2.44	23.66 (4.97)	24.25 (5.02)	23.96 (4.99)
T_{12}	2.44	2.56	2.50	25.25 (5.12)	25.53 (5.15)	25.39 (5.14)
T_{13}	2.49	2.60	2.55	25.26 (5.12)	25.50 (5.15)	25.38 (5.13
T_{14}	2.43	2.57	2.50	24.73 (5.07)	25.01 (5.10)	24.87 (5.09)
T_{15}	2.48	2.59	2.53	25.49 (5.15)	25.75 (5.17)	25.62 (5.16)
T_{16}	2.51	2.62	2.56	25.17 (5.12)	25.36 (5.13)	25.27 (5.13)
T_{17}	2.53	2.60	2.57	24.77 (5.08)	25.05 (5.10)	24.91 (5.09)
$C.D_{(0.05)}$	0.05	NS	0.12	0.07	0.07	0.05

Figures within the parentheses are transformed means.

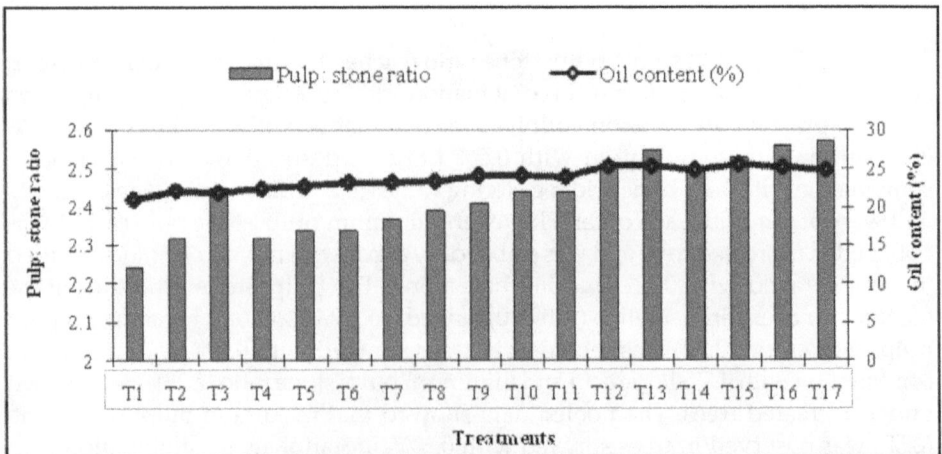

Fig. 3: Effect of girdling, zinc and boron on pulp: stone ratio and oil content of olive cv. Frontoio (Pooled data)

4.1.7.2 Oil content

Application of 0.6% zinc sulphate in combination with 0.4% boric acid resulted in highest oil content of 25.49 per cent which was significantly higher as compared to all other treatments tried during the year 2008-09, whereas minimum oil content of 21.23 per cent was extracted from fruits of untreated trees. During the second year of investigation, application of 0.6% zinc sulphate in combination with 0.4% boric acid resulted in significantly higher oil content (25.75%) as compared to all other treatments tried in this study while, it was minimum (20.68%) in control. From the pooled data it is evident that highest oil content (25.62%) was in fruits from trees sprayed with 0.6% zinc sulphate in combination with 0.4% boric acid, which was significantly higher than all other treatments. The minimum oil content of 20.96 percent was recovered from fruits of untreated trees.

4.1.8 Leaf N, P, K, Ca and Mg

The data regarding the effect of girdling, zinc and boron applied singly or in combination with each other on leaf N, P, K, Ca and Mg content of olive trees are presented in the Table-9 and 10.

Table 9: Effect of girdling, zinc and boron on total leaf N and P content in olive cv. Frontoio.

Treatment	N (%)			P (%)		
	2008-09	2009-10	Pooled	2008-09	2009-10	Pooled
T_1	1.63 (1.62)	1.53 (1.59)	1.58 (1.60)	0.226 (1.11)	0.205 (1.10)	0.216 (1.10)
T_2	1.65 (1.63)	1.59 (1.61)	1.62 (1.62)	0.236 (1.11)	0.219 (1.10)	0.227 (1.11)
T_3	1.66 (1.63)	1.56 (1.60)	1.61 (1.62)	0.233 (1.11)	0.216 (1.10)	0.225 (1.11)
T_4	1.69 (1.64)	1.59 (1.61)	1.64 (1.63)	0.236 (1.11)	0.215 (1.10)	0.226 (1.11)
T_5	1.65 (1.63)	1.60 (1.61)	1.62 (1.62)	0.235 (1.11)	0.216 (1.10)	0.226 (1.11)
T_6	1.66 (1.63)	1.58 (1.61)	1.62 (1.62)	0.235 (1.11)	0.213 (1.10)	0.224 (1.11)
T_7	1.66 (1.63)	1.53 (1.59)	1.60 (1.61)	0.235 (1.11)	0.213 (1.10)	0.224 (1.11)
T_8	1.66 (1.63)	1.56 (1.60)	1.61 (1.62)	0.229 (1.10)	0.207 (1.09)	0.219 (1.10)
T_9	1.65 (1.63)	1.57 (1.60)	1.61 (1.62)	0.233 (1.11)	0.218 (1.10)	0.226 (1.11)
T_{10}	1.73 (1.65)	1.63 (1.62)	1.68 (1.64)	0.235 (1.11)	0.212 (1.10)	0.224 (1.11)
T_{11}	1.73 (1.65)	1.63 (1.62)	1.68 (1.64)	0.228 (1.11)	0.209 (1.09)	0.219 (1.10)
T_{12}	1.72 (1.65)	1.63 (1.62)	1.68 (1.64)	0.226 (1.11)	0.214 (1.10)	0.220 (1.10)
T_{13}	1.68 (1.64)	1.53 (1.58)	1.61 (1.61	0.233 (1.11)	0.214 (1.10)	0.223 (1.10)
T_{14}	1.68 (1.63)	1.53 (1.59)	1.61 (1.61)	0.23 (1.10)	0.210 (1.10)	0.220 (1.10)
T_{15}	1.71 (1.64)	1.58 (1.61)	1.64 (1.63)	0.234 (1.11)	0.211 (1.10)	0.222 (1.10)
T_{16}	1.73 (1.65)	1.59 (1.61)	1.66 (1.63)	0.23 (1.11)	0.212 (1.10)	0.221 (1.11)
T_{17}	1.70 (1.64)	1.55 (1.60)	1.63 (1.62)	0.231 (1.11)	0.213 (1.10)	0.222 (1.10)
$C.D_{(0.05)}$	NS	NS	NS	NS	NS	NS

Figures within the parentheses are transformed means

4.1.8.1 Leaf N

It is clear from the data given in Table 9 that leaf N was not significantly affected by different treatments during 2008-09 as well as in 2009-10. Highest leaf N of 1.73 per cent was recorded in trees that received spray of 0.4% zinc sulphate in combination with 0.5% boric acid, 0.4% zinc sulphate in combination with 0.6% boric acid and 0.6% zinc sulphate in combination with 0.5% boric acid whereas, lowest leaf N (1.63%) was obtained in untreated trees during the year 2008-09. The leaf N varied between 1.53 and 1.63 percent with all the treatments tried during the second year of experimentation. Perusal of the pooled data showed that highest leaf N of 1.68 per cent was observed in trees sprayed with 0.4% zinc sulphate in combination with 0.5% boric acid, 0.4% zinc sulphate in combination with 0.6% boric acid, and 0.5% zinc sulphate in combination with 0.4% boric acid, whereas, lowest leaf N (1.58%) was found in untreated trees.

4.1.8.2 Leaf P

The data presented in Table 9 showed that leaf P was not affected significantly by different treatments. The leaf P varied from 0.226 to 0.236 percent for different treatments during the first year of investigation. During the second year also, not much variation in leaf P was observed among different treatments and it ranged from 0.205 to 0.219 percent. The perusal of the pooled data showed that leaf P was highest (0.227%) in girdled trees and lowest (0.216%) in untreated trees.

4.1.8.3 Leaf K

The leaf K was significantly affected by zinc and boron applied singly or in combination with each other and girdling during both the years of investigations (Table 10). During 2008-09, highest leaf K (1.85%) was obtained in trees sprayed with 0.5% zinc sulphate in combination with 0.4% boric acid closely followed by trees sprayed with 0.4% zinc sulphate in combination with 0.6% boric acid, 0.4% zinc sulphate in combination with 0.5% boric acid, 0.4% zinc sulphate in combination with 0.4% boric acid, 0.6% boric acid applied singly and 0.6% Zinc sulphate in combination with 0.6% boric acid and were at par with each other. Lowest leaf K (1.67%) was estimated from leaves of untreated trees. Similar pattern of variation in leaf K in response to different treatments was observed during the second year of investigation wherein, highest leaf K (1.63%) was observed in trees sprayed with 0.5% zinc sulphate in combination with 0.4% boric acid and lowest (1.47%) in untreated trees. In the pooled data, highest leaf K content of 1.74 percent was found with the application of 0.5% zinc sulphate in combination with 0.4% boric acid closely followed by trees sprayed with 0.4% zinc sulphate in combination with 0.6% boric acid (1.73%), 0.4% zinc sulphate in combination with 0.5% boric acid (1.72%), 0.4% zinc sulphate in combination with 0.4% boric acid (1.72%), 0.6% boric acid applied singly (1.72%) and 0.6% zinc sulphate in combination with 0.6% boric acid (1.72%). The lowest leaf K content (1.57%) was observed in untreated trees.

4.1.8.4 Leaf Ca

It is clear from the data presented in Table 12 that trees receiving 0.5% zinc sulphate in combination with 0.4% boric acid and 0.6% zinc sulphate in combination with 0.4% boric acid exhibited highest leaf Ca of 1.82 percent closely followed by trees which were sprayed with 0.5% zinc sulphate in combination with 0.5% boric acid (1.81%), and 0.5% zinc sulphate in combination with 0.6% boric acid and 0.6% zinc sulphate in combination with 0.5% boric acid (1.80%) and were at par with each other. The lowest leaf Ca of 1.61 percent was recorded in untreated trees. During second year, highest leaf Ca of 1.61 percent was recorded in trees which were sprayed with 0.5% zinc sulphate in combination with 0.5% boric acid and 0.6% zinc sulphate in combination with 0.4% boric acid. Lowest leaf Ca (1.39%) was recorded in untreated trees. The pooled data also showed that highest leaf Ca (1.72%) was found in the leaves of trees sprayed with 0.6% zinc sulphate in combination with 0.4% boric acid closely followed by trees sprayed with 0.5% zinc sulphate in combination with 0.5% boric acid and 0.5% zinc sulphate in combination with 0.4% boric acid, and 0.6% zinc sulphate in combination with 0.5% boric acid registering leaf Ca of 1.71, 1.71and 1.70 percent, respectively and were at par with each other whereas, minimum leaf Ca (1.50%) was found in untreated trees.

Table 10:   Effect of girdling, zinc and boron on total leaf K, Ca, and Mg in olive cv. Frontoio

Treatment	K (%)			Ca (%)			Mg (%)		
	2008-09	2009-10	Pooled	2008-09	2009-10	Pooled	2008-09	2009-10	Pooled
T_1	1.67	1.47	1.57	1.61	1.39	1.50	0.146	0.124	0.135
	(1.64)	(1.57)	(1.60)	(1.61)	(1.55)	(1.58)	(1.07)	(1.06)	(1.06)
T_2	1.77	1.57	1.67	1.72	1.51	1.62	0.151	0.131	0.141
	(1.66)	(1.60)	(1.63)	(1.65)	(1.58)	(1.62)	(1.07)	(1.06)	(1.07)
T_3	1.78	1.56	1.67	1.71	1.50	1.60	0.156	0.134	0.145
	(1.67)	(1.60)	(1.63)	(1.65)	(1.58)	(1.61)	(1.08)	(1.06)	(1.07)
T_4	1.79	1.55	1.67	1.74	1.53	1.63	0.159	0.137	0.148
	(1.67)	(1.60)	(1.63)	(1.65)	(1.59)	(1.62)	(1.08)	(1.07)	(1.07)
T_5	1.79	1.59	1.69	1.76	1.54	1.65	0.161	0.138	0.149
	(1.67)	(1.61)	(1.64)	(1.66)	(1.59)	(1.63)	(1.08)	(1.07)	(1.07)
T_6	1.80	1.58	1.69	1.78	1.55	1.66	0.157	0.135	0.146
	(1.67)	(1.61)	(1.64)	(1.67)	(1.60)	(1.63)	(1.07)	(1.06)	(1.07)
T_7	1.81	1.60	1.70	1.75	1.54	1.65	0.159	0.137	0.148
	(1.68)	(1.61)	(1.64)	(1.66)	(1.59)	(1.63)	(1.08)	(1.07)	(1.07)
T_8	1.83	1.62	1.72	1.75	1.55	1.65	0.158	0.135	0.147
	(1.68)	(1.62)	(1.65)	(1.66)	(1.60)	(1.63)	(1.08)	(1.06)	(1.07)
T_9	1.83	1.61	1.72	1.78	1.55	1.67	0.157	0.134	0.146
	(1.68)	(1.61)	(1.65)	(1.67)	(1.59)	(1.63)	(1.08)	(1.06)	(1.07)
T_{10}	1.84	1.60	1.72	1.78	1.57	1.68	0.159	0.138	0.148
	(1.68)	(1.61)	(1.65)	(1.67)	(1.60)	(1.64)	(1.08)	(1.07)	(1.07)
T_{11}	1.84	1.61	1.73	1.77	1.55	1.66	0.161	0.139	0.150

Contd...

Table-10 Contd...

Treatment	K (%)			Ca (%)			Mg (%)		
	2008-09	2009-10	Pooled	2008-09	2009-10	Pooled	2008-09	2009-10	Pooled
	(1.68)	(1.62)	(1.65)	(1.66)	(1.60)	(1.63)	(1.08)	(1.07)	(1.07)
T_{12}	1.85	1.63	1.74	1.82	1.59	1.71	0.158	0136	0.147
	(1.60)	(1.62)	(1.65)	(1.68)	(1.61)	(1.64)	(1.08)	(1.07)	(1.07)
T_{13}	1.82	1.59	1.71	1.81	1.61	1.71	0.160	0.138	0.149
	(1.68)	(1.61)	(1.64)	(1.68)	(1.61)	(1.64)	(1.08)	(1.07)	(1.07)
T_{14}	1.81	1.59	1.70	1.80	1.56	1.68	0.162	0.140	0.151
	(1.67)	(1.61)	(1.64)	(1.67)	(1.60)	(1.64)	(1.08)	(1.07)	(1.07)
T_{15}	1.81	1.60	1.71	1.82	1.61	1.72	0.161	0.138	0.150
	(1.68)	(1.61)	(1.64)	(1.68)	(1.62)	(1.65)	(1.08)	(1.07)	(1.07)
T_{16}	1.82	1.60	1.71	1.80	1.59	1.70	0.163	0.142	0.153
	(1.68)	(1.61)	(1.65)	(1.67)	(1.61)	(1.64)	(1.08)	(1.07)	(1.07)
T_{17}	1.83	1.61	1.72	1.78	1.57	1.68	0.164	0.143	0.154
	(1.68)	(1.61)	(1.65)	(1.67)	(1.60)	(1.64)	(1.08)	(1.07)	(1.07)
$C.D_{(0.05)}$	0.02	0.02	0.02	0.02	0.03	0.02	NS	NS	0.003

Figures within the parentheses are transformed means

4.1.8.5 Leaf Mg

The perusal of the data presented in Table 12 revealed that leaf Mg was not significantly affected by application of different treatments during both the years of study. However, it is evident from the pooled data that leaf Mg was significantly affected by the application of zinc and boron applied singly or in combination with each other and girdling wherein highest leaf Mg (0.154%) was observed in trees sprayed with 0.6% zinc sulphate in combination with 0.6% boric acid closely followed by trees sprayed with 0.6% zinc sulphate in combination with 0.5% boric acid, and 0.5% zinc sulphate in combination with 0.6% boric acid registering values of 0.153, 0.151 percent, respectively and were at par with each other. The lowest leaf Mg content (0.135%) was found in untreated trees.

4.2 EFFECT OF GROWTH RETARDANTS (PACLOBUTRAZOL AND CHLORMEQUAT) ON GROWTH AND FRUITFULNESS OF OLIVE CV. FRONTOIO.

4.2.1 Growth characteristics

The data pertaining to effect of different growth retardants on growth characteristics of olive trees in terms of increase in trunk circumference, shoot extension growth and relative growth rate are presented in Table-11.

Table 11: Effect of growth retardants on increase in trunk circumference, shoot extension growth and relative growth rate of olive cv. Frontoio.

Treatment	Increase in trunk circumference(%)			Shoot extension growth (cm)			Relative growth rate (cm cm^{-1} month^{-1})		
	2008-09	2009-10	Pooled	2008-09	2009-10	Pooled	2008-09	2009-10	Pooled
T$_1$	6.18	7.18	6.68	12.51	12.53	12.52	0.067	0.049	0.058
T$_2$	8.44	8.50	8.47	9.75	9.42	9.58	0.043	0.040	0.042
T$_3$	7.51	7.80	7.65	8.98	9.26	9.12	0.045	0.035	0.040
T$_4$	7.26	7.83	7.55	7.83	8.65	8.24	0.039	0.036	0.037
T$_5$	8.63	9.37	9.00	9.38	8.95	9.16	0.039	0.036	0.038
T$_6$	7.83	8.56	8.20	7.89	8.02	7.96	0.034	0.031	0.033
T$_7$	8.34	8.85	8.59	7.41	7.89	7.65	0.031	0.032	0.032
T$_8$	8.86	9.30	9.08	10.19	9.52	9.85	0.043	0.038	0.040
T$_9$	8.37	8.82	8.59	8.74	8.33	8.53	0.038	0.033	0.036
T$_{10}$	7.11	7.86	7.48	8.42	7.65	8.03	0.038	0.030	0.034
C.D $_{(0.05)}$	1.25	NS	0.92	0.75	0.66	0.48	0.009	0.007	0.006

4.2.1.1 Increase in trunk circumference

Increase in trunk circumference was significantly influenced by application of different growth retardants. During 2008-09, maximum increase in trunk circumference (8.86%) was recorded with foliar application of 500 ppm chlormequat and was at par with values recorded with foliar application of 500 ppm paclobutrazol (8.63%), soil application of 2 g a.i tree^{-1} paclobutrazol (8.44%), foliar application of 1000 ppm chlormequat (8.37%), foliar application of 2000 ppm paclobutrazol (8.34%), and foliar application of 1000 ppm paclobutrazol (7.83%). The minimum increase in trunk circumference (6.18%) was recorded in untreated trees. In the second year of experimentation (2009-10), the effect of different growth retardants on increase in trunk circumference was non-significant wherein maximum increase of 9.37 percent was recorded with foliar application of 500 ppm paclobutrazol and minimum (7.18%) in untreated trees of olive. As evident from the pooled data, the growth retardants exerted significant influence on the increase in trunk circumference wherein maximum increase in trunk circumference (9.08%) was observed with the foliar application of 500 ppm chlormequat closely followed by foliar application of 500 ppm paclobutrazol, 2000 ppm paclobutrazol and 1000 ppm chlormequat, soil application of 2g a.i tree^{-1} paclobutrazol and foliar application of 1000 ppm paclobutrazol registering trunk circumference increase of 9.00, 8.59, 8.47 and 8.20 percent, respectively and were at par with each other whereas, minimum increase in trunk circumference (6.68%) was found in untreated trees.

4.2.1.2 Shoot extension growth

Shoot extension growth was significantly reduced by different growth retardant treatments during both the years of investigation. An inquisition of the data showed that minimum shoot extension growth of 7.41 cm was measured from trees sprayed with 2000 ppm paclobutrazol which was at par with values recorded with soil application of 6 g a.i tree^{-1} paclobutrazol (7.83 cm) and foliar application of 1000 ppm paclobutrazol (7.89 cm) during 2008-09. Significantly higher shoot extension growth of 12.51 cm was recorded in untreated trees. However, during the second year foliar application of 2000 ppm chlormequat exhibited most dwarfing effect and recorded minimum shoot extension growth of 7.65 cm, closely followed by foliar application of 2000 ppm paclobutrazol and 1000 ppm paclobutrazol with the values of 7.89 and 8.02 cm, respectively and were at par with each other, whereas maximum shoot extension growth of 12.53 cm was obtained in untreated trees. From the pooled data it can be inferred that there was a progressive decrease in shoot extension growth with the increasing concentration of growth retardant used in this study. The untreated trees recorded significantly higher shoot extension growth of 12.52 cm as compared to all other treatments tried in this study. Minimum shoot extension growth of 7.65 cm was observed in trees sprayed with 2000 ppm paclobutrazol closely followed by foliar application of 1000 ppm paclobutrazol and 2000 ppm chlormequat registering shoot extension growth of 7.96 and 8.03 cm, respectively which were at par with each other.

4.2.1.3 Relative growth rate (RGR)

The growth retardants had a significant effect on relative growth rate during 2008-09 as well as 2009-10. There was a progressive decrease in RGR with the increasing concentrations of growth retardants tried under the present investigation. The untreated trees recorded maximum RGR (0.067 cmcm^{-1}month^{-1}) which was significantly higher than all other treatments. Minimum RGR of 0.031 cm cm^{-1} month^{-1} was observed with foliar application of 2000 ppm paclobutrazol which was at par with all other treatments of different growth retardants. During second year of investigation, minimum RGR of 0.030 cm cm^{-1} month^{-1} was recorded in trees sprayed with 2000 ppm chlormequat and significantly higher RGR of 0.049 cm cm^{-1} month^{-1} was recorded in untreated trees. Pooled data also showed effect of different growth retardants on the RGR, wherein, untreated trees had significantly higher relative growth rate (0.058 cm cm^{-1} month^{-1}) than all other treatments tried. There was progressive decrease in RGR with the increasing dose of growth retardants. The minimum RGR (0.032 cm cm^{-1} month^{-1}) was found with foliar application of 2000 ppm paclobutrazol, closely followed by foliar application of 1000 ppm paclobutrazol, 2000 ppm chlormequat, 1000 ppm chlormequat, soil application of 6 g a.i. tree^{-1} paclobutrazol, and 500 ppm paclobutrazol registering RGR of 0.033, 0.034, 0.036, 0.037, and 0.038 cm cm^{-1} month^{-1} respectively and were at par with each other.

4.2.2 Leaf area, unit leaf area and specific leaf area

The data on the effect of growth retardants on leaf area, unit leaf area and specific leaf area are presented in the Table 12.

4.2.2.1 Leaf area

Leaf area was significantly reduced with the increasing doses of different growth retardants during the present investigation. Minimum leaf area (2.85 cm^2) was recorded with foliar application of 2000 ppm paclobutrazol closely followed by soil application of 6 g a.i tree^{-1} paclobutrazol wherein, leaf area of 2.91 cm^2 was recorded which were at par with each other. The untreated trees recorded significantly higher leaf area of 3.84 cm^2 as compared to all other treatments. During the second year (2009-10) of experimental trial, minimum leaf area of 2.94 cm^2 was recorded with soil application of 6 g a.i tree^{-1} paclobutrazol and was at par with foliar application of 2000 ppm paclobutrazol and soil application of 4 g a.i tree^{-1} paclobutrazol wherein, leaf area of 3.01and 3.04 cm^2, respectively was observed. The perusal of the pooled data showed maximum leaf area (3.84 cm^2) in untreated trees. However, minimum leaf area (2.93 cm^2) was obtained with soil application of 6 g a.i tree^{-1} paclobutrazol and foliar application of 2000 ppm paclobutrazol.

Table 12: Effect of growth retardants on leaf area, unit leaf area and specific leaf area in olive cv. Frontoio

Treatment	Leaf area(cm^2)			Unit leaf area(cm^2)			Specific leaf area(cm^2 g^{-1})		
	2008-09	2009-10	Pooled	2008-09	2009-10	Pooled	2008-09	2009-10	Pooled
T$_1$	3.84	3.83	3.84	3.84	3.58	3.71	4.75	4.86	4.80
T$_2$	3.31	3.27	3.29	3.31	3.08	3.19	4.14	4.23	4.19
T$_3$	3.09	3.04	3.07	3.09	3.04	3.07	4.37	4.40	4.39
T$_4$	2.91	2.94	2.93	2.91	2.94	2.93	4.27	4.47	4.37
T$_5$	3.34	3.39	3.36	3.35	3.39	3.37	5.09	4.33	4.71
T$_6$	3.02	3.15	3.08	3.02	3.15	3.09	3.55	4.49	4.02
T$_7$	2.85	3.01	2.93	2.86	3.01	2.93	4.07	3.95	4.01
T$_8$	3.47	3.46	3.46	3.47	3.46	3.46	4.57	4.41	4.49
T$_9$	3.28	3.34	3.31	3.28	3.37	3.33	4.52	5.07	4.79
T$_{10}$	3.17	3.16	3.17	3.18	3.16	3.17	4.64	4.26	4.45
C.D $_{(0.05)}$	0.14	0.20	0.12	0.14	0.30	0.16	NS	NS	NS

4.2.2.2 Unit leaf area

Unit leaf area was significantly affected with the application of different growth retardants during both years of experimentation. During 2008-09, unit leaf area was significantly reduced with the foliar application of 2000 ppm paclobutrazol exhibiting unit leaf area of 2.86 cm^2 closely followed by soil application of 6 g a.i tree^{-1} paclobutrazol wherein, unit leaf area of 2.91 cm^2 was recorded and both were at par with each other whereas significantly higher unit leaf area of 3.84 cm^2 was obtained in untreated trees of olive. During 2009-10, a progressive decrease in unit leaf area with application of different growth retardants tried in the present study was observed. Minimum unit leaf area (2.94 cm^2) was recorded with soil application of 6 g a.i tree^{-1} paclobutrazol closely followed by foliar application of 2000 ppm paclobutrazol, soil application of 4 g a.i tree^{-1} paclobutrazol, 2 g a.i tree^{-1} paclobutrazol, foliar application of 1000 ppm paclobutrazol and foliar application of 2000 ppm chlormequat registering values of 3.01, 3.04, 3.08, 3.15, 3.16 cm^2, respectively and were at par with each other whereas, maximum unit leaf area (3.58 cm^2) was recorded in untreated trees. It is clear from the pooled data that minimum unit leaf area (2.93 cm^2) was observed with soil application of 6 g a.i tree^{-1} paclobutrazol and foliar application of 2000 ppm paclobutrazol and were at par with unit leaf area observed with soil application of 4 g a.i tree^{-1} paclobutrazol, and foliar application of 1000 ppm paclobutrazol exhibiting respective values of 3.07 and 3.09 cm^2.

4.2.2.3 Specific leaf area

The specific leaf area was not significantly affected by application of different growth retardants during both the years of experimentation. The maximum specific leaf area (5.09 cm^2 g^{-1}) was recorded with foliar application of 500 ppm paclobutrazol and minimum (3.55 cm^2 g^{-1}) with 1000 ppm paclobutrazol during 2008-09. During 2009-10, specific leaf area ranged from 3.95 to 5.07 cm^2 g^{-1} for different treatments tried in the present investigations. The pooled data also exhibited non-significant effect of different growth retardants on specific leaf area wherein, minimum specific leaf area (4.01cm^2 g^{-1}) was observed with foliar application of 2000 ppm paclobutrazol and maximum (4.80 cm^2 g^{-1}) in control.

4.2.3 Leaf water content, stomatal count and chlorophyll content

The data pertaining to above mentioned parameters is presented in the Table 13.

4.2.3.1 Leaf water content

Leaf water content was significantly affected by different treatments of growth retardants. During the first year (2008-09), soil application of 4 g a.i tree^{-1} paclobutrazol resulted in highest leaf water content of 63.54 per cent closely followed by foliar application of 500 ppm chlormequat, untreated trees and foliar application of 1000 ppm paclobutrazol, registering leaf water content of 63.07, 61.27 and 60.09 percent, respectively and were at par with each other. Lowest leaf water content of 53.62 per cent was obtained with soil application of 2 g a.i tree^{-1} paclobutrazol. However, in the second year, untreated trees resulted in highest leaf water content of 63.90 per cent closely followed by foliar application of 500 ppm chlormequat, 1000 ppm chlormequat, and 1000 ppm paclobutrazol registering leaf water content of 62.66, 62.53, and 61.41 percent, respectively. The lowest leaf water content (55.45%) was observed with soil application of 6 g a.i tree^{-1} paclobutrazol. Pooled data also showed significant influence of different growth retardants on leaf water content. Highest leaf water content (62.87%) was obtained with the foliar application of 500 ppm chlormequat closely followed by untreated trees, soil application of 4 g a.i tree^{-1} paclobutrazol, foliar application of 1000 ppm paclobutrazol and 1000 ppm chlormequat, registering leaf water content of 62.59, 61.99, 60.75, and 60.43 percent, respectively and were at par with each other whereas, lowest leaf water content (56.24%) was recorded in trees sprayed with 2000 ppm chlormequat.

Table 13: Effect of growth retardants on leaf water content, stomatal count and chlorophyll content in olive cv. Frontoio.

Treatment	Leaf water content (%)			Stomatal count (number/ microscopic field)			Chlorophyll content (mg/g)		
	2008-09	2009-10	Pooled	2008-09	2009-10	Pooled	2008-09	2009-10	Pooled
T_1	61.27	63.90	62.59	20.25	21.25	20.75	1.07	1.05	1.06
T_2	53.62	59.29	56.45	22.50	22.50	22.50	0.99	1.03	1.02
T_3	63.54	60.45	61.99	22.58	23.00	22.79	1.14	1.16	1.15
T_4	57.94	55.45	56.69	20.75	20.75	20.75	1.13	1.15	1.14
T_5	59.23	59.55	59.39	24.17	24.83	24.50	1.27	1.28	1.27
T_6	60.09	61.41	60.75	22.58	23.42	23.00	1.24	1.24	1.24
T_7	56.55	58.15	57.35	21.25	22.33	21.79	1.22	1.22	1.22
T_8	63.07	62.66	62.87	22.92	23.83	23.37	1.40	1.43	1.42
T_9	58.34	62.53	60.43	21.58	22.67	22.12	1.38	1.35	1.36
T_{10}	55.77	56.72	56.24	20.58	21.42	21.00	1.36	1.42	1.39
$C.D_{(0.05)}$	4.26	3.14	2.56	0.81	1.00	0.62	0.13	0.15	0.09

4.2.3.2 Stomatal count

In the first year of study olive trees receiving spray of 500 ppm paclobutrazol resulted in maximum stomatal count of 24.17 number/microscopic field which was significantly higher than all other treatments, whereas, minimum stomatal count (20.25 number/microscopic field) was recorded in untreated trees. During second year (2009-10) of study, maximum stomatal count (24.83 number/microscopic field) was recorded in trees sprayed with 500 ppm paclobutrazol and was significantly higher than all other treatments tried. However, minimum stomatal count (20.75 number/microscopic field) was recorded with the soil application of 6 g a.i tree^{-1} paclobutrazol. The pooled data showed maximum stomatal count (24.50 number/ microscopic field) in trees sprayed with 500 ppm paclobutrazol which was significantly higher than all other treatments. Minimum stomatal count (20.75 number/microscopic field) was recorded in untreated trees and soil application of 6 g a.i tree^{-1} paclobutrazol and was at par with stomatal count (21 number/microscopic field) recorded in trees sprayed with 2000 ppm chlormequat.

4.2.3.3 Chlorophyll content

Highest chlorophyll content of 1.40 mg/g was recorded with foliar application of 500 ppm chlormequat closely followed foliar application of 1000 ppm chlormequat, 2000 ppm chlormequat and 500 ppm paclobutrazol registering chlorophyll content of 1.38, 1.36 and 1.27 mg/g, respectively and were at par with each other. Minimum chlorophyll content of 0.99 mg/g was estimated with the soil application of 2 g a.i tree^{-1} paclobutrazol. During second year (2009-10) of experimentation, highest chlorophyll (1.43 mg/g) was recorded with foliar application of 500 ppm chlormequat closely followed by foliar application of 2000 ppm chlormequat, 1000 ppm chlormequat and 500 ppm paclobutrazol registering chlorophyll content of 1.42, 1.35

and 1.28 mg/g, respectively and was at par with each other. The perusal of the pooled data showed that significantly higher total leaf chlorophyll content (1.42 mg/g) was found in trees sprayed with 500 ppm chlormequat as compared to control, and was at par with the chlorophyll content observed with foliar application of 2000 ppm chlormequat and 1000 ppm chlormequat whereas, minimum leaf chlorophyll content (1.02 mg/g) was obtained with the soil application of 2 g a.i tree^{-1} paclobutrazol.

4.2.4 Flowering characteristics

The data pertaining to duration of flowering, blooming intensity and proportion of perfect flowers as affected by different growth retardants is tabulated in Table 14 and depicted in fig.4 and plate 2.

4.2.4.1 Duration of flowering

The perusal of the data revealed that duration of flowering was significantly reduced with the progressive increase in the concentration of different growth retardants during both the years of study. In the first year (2008-09) of experimental trial, minimum duration of flowering (16.67 days) was observed with foliar application of 2000 ppm chlormequat and was significantly lower than all other treatments whereas maximum duration of flowering (19.33 days) was recorded in untreated trees. During 2009-10, duration of flowering was reduced by 3.34 days with the soil application of 6 g a.i tree-1 paclobutrazol from 19.67 days to 16.33 days. The pooled data showed maximum duration of flowering (19.50 days) in untreated trees which was significantly higher than all other treatments tried. The minimum duration of flowering (16.67 days) was obtained with soil application of 6 g a.i tree-1 paclobutrazol. Thus, there was a reduction of 2.83 days in duration of flowering with soil application of 6 g a.i tree-1 paclobutrazol as compared to control.

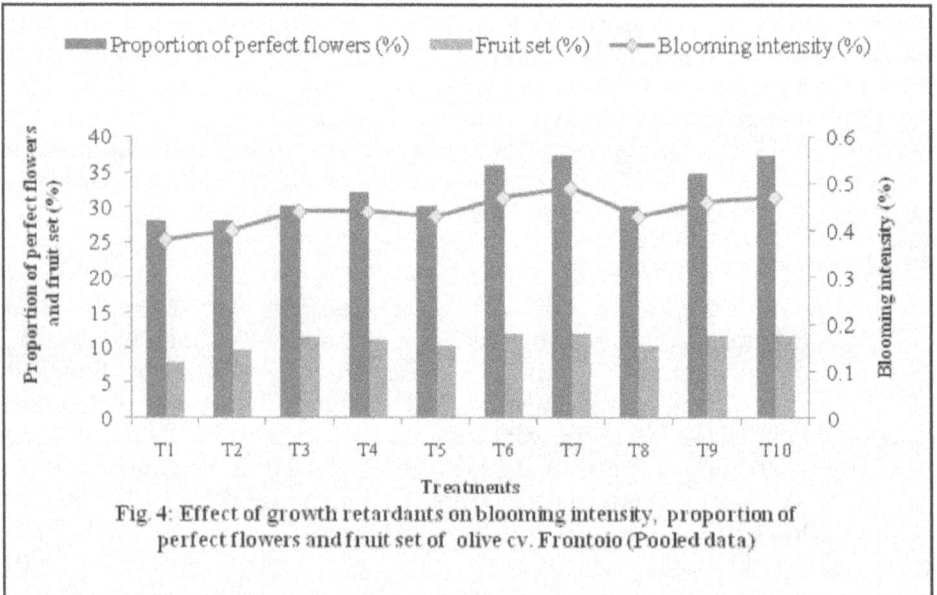

Fig. 4: Effect of growth retardants on blooming intensity, proportion of perfect flowers and fruit set of olive cv. Frontoio (Pooled data)

Table 14: Effect of growth retardants on duration of flowering, blooming intensity, and proportion of perfect flowers in olive cv. Frontoio1

Treatment	Duration of flowering (days)			Blooming Intensity(%)			Proportion of perfect flowers (%)		
	2008-09	2009-10	Pooled	2008-09	2009-10	Pooled	2008-09	2009-10	Pooled
T_1	19.33 (4.51)	19.67 (4.55)	19.50 (4.53)	0.44(1.20)	0.32(1.15)	0.38(1.17)	26.67(31.06)	29.33(32.77)	28.00(31.92)
T_2	18.00 (4.36)	17.67 (4.32)	17.83 (4.34)	0.46(1.21)	0.33(1.15)	0.40(1.18)	25.33(30.19)	30.67(33.60)	28.00(31.90)
T_3	17.67 (4.32)	17.33 (4.28)	17.50 (4.30)	0.53(1.24)	0.35(1.16)	0.44(1.20)	29.33(32.77)	30.67(33.60)	30.00(33.19)
T_4	17.00 (4.24)	16.33 (4.16)	16.67 (4.20)	0.52(1.23)	0.37(1.17)	0.44(1.20)	30.67(33.60)	33.33(35.24)	32.00(34.42)
T_5	17.33 (4.28)	18.00 (4.36)	17.67 (4.32)	0.50(1.23)	0.35(1.16)	0.43(1.19)	29.33(32.77)	30.67(33.60)	30.00(33.19)
T_6	17.33 (4.28)	17.00 (4.24)	17.17 (4.26)	0.56(1.25)	0.39(1.18)	0.47(1.21)	34.67(36.05)	37.33(37.64)	36.00(36.84)
T_7	17.00 (4.24)	17.00 (4.24)	17.00 (4.24)	0.57(1.25)	0.41(1.19)	0.49(1.22)	36.00(36.84)	38.67(38.43)	37.33(37.63)
T_8	17.67 (4.32)	18.33 (4.40)	18.00 (4.36)	0.50(1.23)	0.36(1.17)	0.43(1.19)	29.33(32.77)	30.67(33.60)	30.00(33.19)
T_9	17.00 (4.24)	17.33 (4.28)	17.17 (4.26)	0.53(1.24)	0.39(1.18)	0.46(1.21)	33.33(35.24)	36.00(36.84)	34.67(36.04)
T_{10}	16.67 (4.20)	17.00 (4.24)	16.83 (4.22)	0.55(1.24)	0.40(1.18)	0.47(1.21)	37.33(37.64)	37.33(37.64)	37.33(37.64)
C.D (0.05)	0.15	0.15	0.10	0.007	0.007	0.005	2.36	2.70	1.73

Figures within the parentheses are transformed means.

Plate 4: Flowering in olive trees sprayed with 1000 ppm paclobutrazol

4.2.4.2 Blooming intensity

There was a significant effect of different growth retardants on blooming intensity during 2008-09 and 2009-10. During the first year of study, highest blooming intensity of 0.57 percent was recorded in trees sprayed with 2000 ppm paclobutrazol and was at par with the blooming intensity of 0.56 percent recorded in trees sprayed with 1000 ppm paclobutrazol. Lowest blooming intensity of 0.44 percent was observed in untreated trees. However, during the second year, there was an overall decrease in the intensity of flowering under all treatments wherein the blooming intensity ranged from 0.32 to 0.41 percent with highest value (0.41%) recorded in trees sprayed with 2000 ppm paclobutrazol closely followed by blooming intensity of 0.40 percent recorded in trees sprayed with 2000 ppm chlormequat which were at par with each other. The lowest blooming intensity (0.32%) was observed in untreated trees. The pooled data revealed that highest blooming intensity (0.49%) was obtained in trees sprayed with 2000 ppm paclobutrazol which was significantly higher than all other treatments. However, lowest blooming intensity (0.38%) was observed in untreated trees.

4.2.4.3 Proportion of perfect flowers

Different growth retardants significantly influenced the proportion of perfect flowers. In the first year of study, the proportion of perfect flowers reached to a maximum of 37.33 percent in trees sprayed with 2000 ppm chlormequat closely followed by 36.00 percent in trees sprayed with 2000 ppm paclobutrazol whereas, minimum (25.33%) was obtained with soil application of 2 g a.i tree-1 paclobutrazol and was at par with proportion of perfect flowers (26.67%) recorded in untreated trees. During the second year (2009-10), maximum proportion of perfect flowers (38.67%) was recorded in trees sprayed with 2000 ppm paclobutrazol, closely followed by trees sprayed with 1000 ppm paclobutrazol and 2000 ppm chlormequat and 1000 ppm chlormequat, registering values of 37.33, 37.33 and 36.00 percent, respectively and were at par with each other. However, minimum proportion of perfect flowers (29.33%) was obtained in untreated trees and was at par with soil application of 2 g a.i tree-1 paclobutrazol, 4 g a.i tree-1 paclobutrazol and foliar application of 500 ppm paclobutrazol. Perusal of the pooled data showed that highest proportion of perfect flowers (37.33%) was observed in trees sprayed with 2000 ppm paclobutrazol and 2000 ppm chlormequat which was at par with the foliar application of 1000 ppm paclobutrazol (36.00%) while, lowest proportion of perfect flowers (28.00%) was found in untreated trees and soil application of 2 g a.i tree-1 paclobutrazol.

4.2.5 Fruiting characteristics

The data pertaining to effect of growth retardants on fruit set, fruit drop and fruit yield of olive cultivar Frontoio is presented in Table 15 and depicted in fig. 5 and plate 5.

4.2.5.1 Fruit set

The perusal of the data reveal that fruit set was significantly affected by different growth retardants during both the years of investigation. In the year 2008-09, fruit set reached to a highest of 14.45 percent with the foliar application of 2000 ppm paclobutrazol and 1000 ppm chlormequat and was at par with fruit set obtained with foliar application of 1000 ppm paclobutrazol. Lowest fruit set of 9.90 percent was recorded in untreated trees. During the second year, there was an overall decrease in the fruit set in all the treatments tried, wherein highest fruit set (9.77%) was recorded in trees sprayed with 1000 ppm paclobutrazol closely followed by 2000 ppm paclobutrazol registering fruit set of 9.74 percent and were at par with each other whereas, lowest fruit set (5.86%) was recorded in untreated trees. The pooled data on fruit set also exhibited significant effect of growth retardants on fruit set and there was an increase in fruit set with increasing doses of different growth retardants. The highest fruit set (12.10%) was observed in trees sprayed with 1000 ppm paclobutrazol which was at par with the fruit set obtained in trees sprayed with 2000 ppm paclobutrazol (12.09%). However, significantly lower fruit set (7.88%) was found in untreated trees as compared to all other treatments.

Table 15: Effect of growth retardants on fruit set, fruit drop, and fruit yield in olive cv. Frontoio

Treatment	Fruit set(%)			Fruit Drop(%)			Fruit Yield(Kg tree⁻¹)		
	2008-09	2009-10	Pooled	2008-09	2009-10	Pooled	2008-09	2009-10	Pooled
T_1	9.90(3.30)	5.86(2.62)	7.88(2.96)	62.22	60.26	61.24	2.05	1.03	1.54
T_2	11.99(3.60)	7.34(2.89)	9.66(3.24)	57.41	56.53	56.97	2.24	1.30	1.77
T_3	14.10(3.89)	8.82(3.13)	11.46(3.51)	55.28	55.80	55.54	2.63	1.61	2.12
T_4	13.05(3.75)	8.91(3.15)	10.98(3.45)	53.72	54.46	54.09	2.72	1.69	2.20
T_5	13.01(3.74)	7.67(2.94)	10.34(3.34)	56.59	55.57	56.08	2.51	1.25	1.88
T_6	14.43(3.93)	9.77(3.28)	12.10(3.60)	52.45	52.46	52.46	2.90	1.56	2.23
T_7	14.45(3.93)	9.74(3.28)	12.09(3.60)	51.41	51.85	51.63	2.92	1.62	2.27
T_8	12.92(3.73)	7.57(2.92)	10.24(3.33)	56.23	58.89	57.56	2.34	1.20	1.77
T_9	14.45(3.93)	8.89(3.14)	11.67(3.54)	53.51	55.74	54.63	2.72	1.45	2.08
T_{10}	14.26(3.91)	9.09(3.17)	11.67(3.54)	52.88	53.76	53.32	2.71	1.49	2.10
C.D $_{(0.05)}$	0.14	0.15	0.10	3.78	NS	3.11	0.14	0.11	0.09

Figures within the parentheses are tratensformed means.

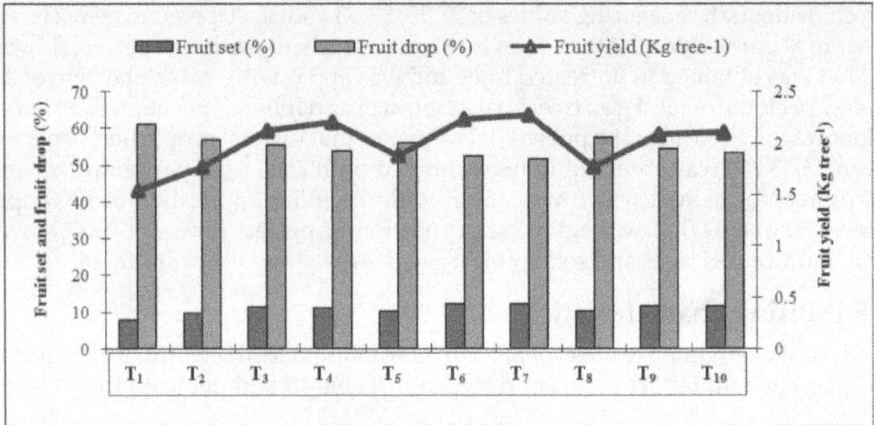

Fig. 5: Effect of growth retardants on fruit set, fruit drop, and fruit yield in olive cv. Frontoio (Pooled data)

4.2.5.2 Fruit drop

Application of growth retardants significantly reduced fruit drop in olive during 2008-09 however, the effect of different growth retardants was non-significant during 2009-10. There was a significant reduction in fruit drop from 62.22 percent to 51.41 percent wherein, highest fruit drop (62.22%) was recorded in untreated trees and lowest in trees sprayed with 2000 ppm paclobutrazol during the first year of experimental trial. During the second year (2009-10) highest fruit drop (60.26%) was recorded in untreated trees and lowest (51.85%) in trees sprayed with 2000 ppm paclobutrazol. The elucidation of pooled data showed positive and significant influence of growth retardants in reduction of per cent fruit drop. The untreated trees exhibited significantly higher fruit drop (61.24%) as compared to all other treatments whereas, trees sprayed with 2000 ppm paclobutrazol exhibited lowest fruit drop (51.63%).

Plat 5: Fruiting in olive trees sprayed with 1000 ppm paclobutrazol

4.2.5.3 Fruit yield

Fruit yield was significantly increased with the application of growth retardants during both the years of investigation. Highest fruit yield (2.92 Kg tree-1) was recorded in trees sprayed with 2000 ppm paclobutrazol closely followed by trees sprayed with 1000 ppm paclobutrazol registering fruit yield of 2.90 Kg tree-1 and were at par with each other whereas, lowest fruit yield (2.05 Kg tree-1) was recorded in untreated trees during the first year of study. In the second year of experimental trial, highest fruit yield (1.69 Kg tree-1) was recorded with soil application of 6 g a.i tree-1 paclobutrazol closely followed by foliar application of 2000 ppm paclobutrazol and soil application of 2g a.i tree-1 paclobutrazol registering fruit yield of 1.62 and 1.61 Kg tree-1, respectively and were at par with each other. There was an overall reduction of fruit yield with all the treatments during the second year as compared to first year of the experimental trial. From the pooled data on fruit yield, it was found that there was an increase in fruit yield of olive with the application of higher doses of growth retardants. The highest fruit yield (2.27 Kg tree-1) was observed with foliar application of 2000 ppm paclobutrazol closely followed by foliar application of 1000 ppm paclobutrazol and soil application of 6 g a.i tree-1 paclobutrazol registering fruit yield of 2.23, and 2.20 Kg tree-1, respectively and were at par with each other. The lowest fruit yield (1.54 Kg tree-1) was found in untreated trees.

4.2.6 Physical parameters of fruits

The data regarding the effect of growth retardants on fruit size, fruit weight and fruit volume is presented in Table 16.

4.2.6.1 Fruit size

There was progressive decrease in fruit size with the increasing doses of different growth retardants. Fruit size ranged from 1.22 cm to 1.55 cm wherein, maximum fruit size (1.55 cm) was recorded with foliar application of 500 ppm paclobutrazol during the first year of investigation. In the second year (2009-10) of experimentation, maximum fruit size (1.63 cm) was recorded with foliar application of 500 ppm chlormequat closely followed by foliar application of 500 ppm paclobutrazol, soil application of 2 g a.i tree-1 paclobutrazol, soil application of 4 g a.i tree-1 paclobutrazol and foliar application of 1000 ppm chlormequat and foliar application of 2000 ppm chlormequat registering fruit size of 1.59, 1.57, 1.52, 1.52 and 1.50 cm, respectively and were at par with each other. Minimum fruit size of 1.27 cm was measured in untreated trees. A glance of the pooled data revealed that maximum fruit size (1.58 cm) was observed with foliar application of 500 ppm chlormequat closely followed by foliar application of 500 ppm paclobutrazol and soil application of 2 g a.i tree-1 paclobutrazol registering fruit size of 1.57 and 1.55 cm, respectively and were at par with each other. Significantly lower fruit size (1.24 cm) was observed in untreated trees as compared to application of different growth retardants.

Table 16: Effect of growth retardants on fruit size, fruit weight and fruit volume of olive cv. Frontolo

Treatment	Fruit size (cm)			Fruit weight (g)			Fruit volume(cc)		
	2008-09	2009-10	Pooled	2008-09	2009-10	Pooled	2008-09	2009-10	Pooled
T1	1.22	1.27	1.24	1.24	1.30	1.27	1.35	1.36	1.35
T2	1.53	1.57	1.55	2.25	2.30	2.28	2.28	2.31	2.29
T3	1.44	1.52	1.48	2.16	2.28	2.22	2.17	2.25	2.21
T4	1.42	1.49	1.45	2.11	2.21	2.16	2.16	2.21	2.18
T5	1.55	1.59	1.57	2.23	2.33	2.28	2.25	2.31	2.28
T6	1.43	1.48	1.45	2.11	2.21	2.16	2.17	2.26	2.21
T7	1.40	1.48	1.44	2.09	2.18	2.14	2.15	2.22	2.19
T8	1.53	1.63	1.58	2.20	2.24	2.22	2.25	2.31	2.28
T9	1.44	1.52	1.48	2.07	2.06	2.06	2.14	2.18	2.16
T10	1.43	1.50	1.46	2.06	2.07	2.06	2.13	2.18	2.15
C.D$_{(0.05)}$	0.12	0.13	0.09	0.12	0.11	0.08	0.12	0.11	0.08

4.2.6.2 Fruit weight

In the first year of experimental trial maximum fruit weight (2.25 g) was obtained with soil application of 2 g a.i tree^{-1} paclobutrazol closely followed by foliar application of 500 ppm paclobutrazol, foliar application of 500 ppm chlormequat and soil application of 4 g a.i tree^{-1} paclobutrazol registering fruit weight of 2.23, 2.20 and 2.16 g, respectively and were at par with each other. The minimum fruit weight of 1.24 g was observed in untreated trees. During the second year (2009-10) of study, fruit weight varied significantly from 1.30 g to 2.33 g registering maximum fruit weight (2.33 g) with foliar application of 500 ppm paclobutrazol and minimum in untreated trees. As evident from the pooled data, maximum fruit weight (2.28 g) was observed with soil application of 2 g a.i tree^{-1} paclobutrazol and foliar application of 500 ppm paclobutrazol closely followed by soil application of 4 g a.i tree^{-1} paclobutrazol and foliar application of 500 ppm chlormequat registering fruit weight of 2.22 and 2.22 g, respectively and were at par with each other. The minimum fruit weight (1.27 g) was obtained in untreated trees.

4.2.6.3 Fruit volume

An inquisition of the data from the Table 18 revealed that maximum fruit volume (2.28 cc) was recorded with soil application of 2 g a.i tree^{-1} paclobutrazol and minimum (1.35 cc) in untreated trees during the first year of experimental trial. The data of second year showed maximum fruit volume (2.31 cc) with the soil application of 2 g a.i tree^{-1} paclobutrazol, foliar application of 500 ppm paclobutrazol and foliar application of 500 ppm chlormequat closely followed by foliar application of 1000 ppm paclobutrazol, soil application of 4 g a.i tree^{-1} paclobutrazol, foliar application of 2000 ppm paclobutrazol, and soil application of 6 g a.i tree^{-1} paclobutrazol registering fruit volume of 2.26, 2.25, 2.22, and 2.21, respectively and were at par with each other. The minimum fruit volume (1.36 cc) was recorded in untreated trees. Perusal of the pooled data showed that fruit volume reached to a maximum of 2.29 cc with the soil application of 2 g a.i tree^{-1} paclobutrazol, closely followed by foliar application of 500 ppm paclobutrazol, 500 ppm chlormequat, soil application of 4 g a.i tree^{-1} paclobutrazol and foliar application of 1000 ppm paclobutrazol registering fruit volume of 2.28, 2.28, 2.21 and 2.21 cc, respectively and were at par with each other. The minimum fruit volume of 1.35 cc was observed in untreated trees.

4.2.7 Pulp: stone ratio and oil content

The data pertaining to the effect of growth retardants on pulp: stone ratio and oil content of olive cultivar Frontoio are presented in Table 19 and depicted in fig. 6.

4.2.7.1 Pulp: stone ratio

Results obtained in the first year of investigations reveal that significantly higher pulp: stone ratio (3.63) was recorded with foliar application of 500 ppm paclobutrazol as compared to all other treatments. The minimum pulp: stone ratio of 2.25 was obtained in untreated trees. The findings of second year also revealed that foliar application of 500 ppm paclobutrazol resulted in highest pulp: stone ratio of 3.68 and was significantly higher as compared to all other treatments. The data when pooled revealed that significantly higher pulp: stone ratio (3.66) was observed in trees sprayed with 500 ppm paclobutrazol as compared to all other treatments. Minimum pulp: stone ratio (2.24) was found in untreated trees.

Table 17: Effect of growth retardants on fruit pulp: stone ratio and oil content of olive cv. Frontoio.

Treatment	Pulp: stone ratio			Oil content(%)		
	2008-09	2009-10	Pooled	2008-09	2009-10	Pooled
T$_1$	2.25(1.80)	2.24(1.80)	2.24(1.80)	20.61(4.65)	21.18(4.71)	20.89(4.68)
T$_2$	3.57(2.14)	3.55(2.13)	3.56(2.13)	25.44(5.14)	25.85(5.18)	25.64(5.16)
T$_3$	3.47(2.11)	3.55(2.13)	3.51(2.12)	23.97(4.99)	24.52(5.05)	24.24(5.02)
T$_4$	3.45(2.11)	3.49(2.12)	3.47(2.11)	23.66(4.96)	24.23(5.02)	23.94(4.99)
T$_5$	3.63(2.15)	3.68(2.16)	3.66(2.16)	25.41(5.14)	25.91(5.19)	25.66(5.16)
T$_6$	3.52(2.13)	3.63(2.15)	3.58(2.14)	23.58(4.96)	24.08(5.01)	23.83(4.98)
T$_7$	3.51(2.12)	3.37(2.09)	3.44(2.11)	22.51(4.85)	22.94(4.89)	22.72(4.87)
T$_8$	3.49(2.12)	3.42(2.10)	3.45(2.11)	24.33(5.03)	24.89(5.09)	24.61(5.06)
T$_9$	3.28(2.07)	3.32(2.08)	3.30(2.07)	23.18(4.92)	23.38(4.94)	23.28(4.93)
T$_{10}$	3.26(2.06)	3.23(2.06)	3.24(2.06)	22.59(4.86)	22.63(4.86)	22.61(4.86)
C.D $_{(0.05)}$	0.03	0.03	0.02	0.18	0.16	0.12

Figures within the parentheses are transformed means.

4.2.7.2 Oil content

During 2008-09 and 2009-10, significantly higher oil content of 25.41 and 25.91 percent, respectively was recorded in trees sprayed with paclobutrazol 500 ppm as compared to all other treatments tested. The minimum oil content of 20.61 and 21.18

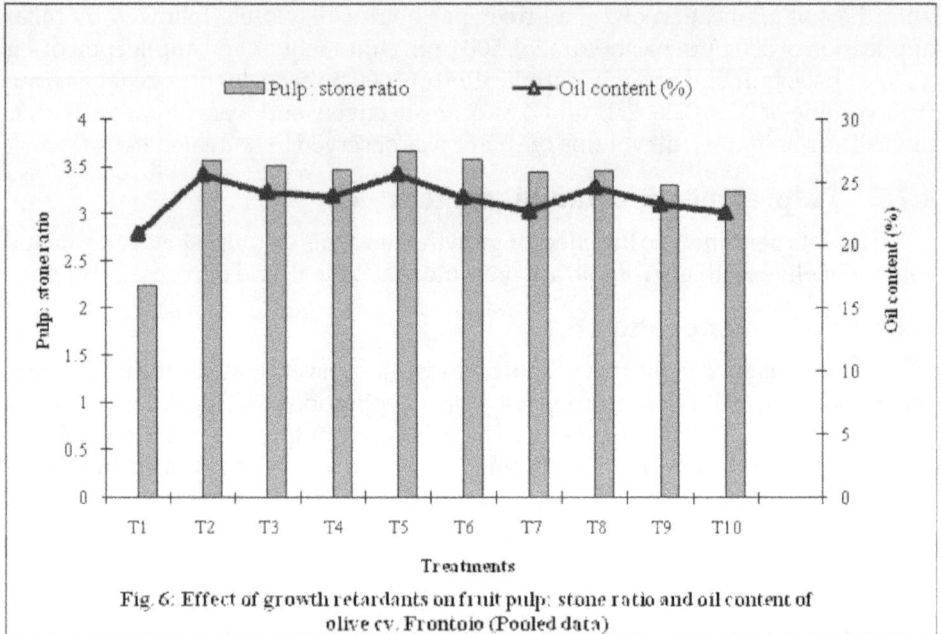

Fig. 6: Effect of growth retardants on fruit pulp: stone ratio and oil content of olive cv. Frontoio (Pooled data)

percent was obtained in untreated trees for first and second years of experimentation, respectively. Similarly, in the pooled data highest oil content (25.66%) was observed with foliar application of 500 ppm paclobutrazol and was at par with oil content of 25.64 percent obtained with soil application of 2 g a.i tree-1 paclobutrazol. Lowest oil content (20.89%) was found in untreated trees.

4.2.8 Leaf N, P, K, Ca and Mg

The data pertaining to the effect of different growth retardants on leaf N, P, K, Ca and Mg is tabulated in Table 18.

4.2.8.1 Leaf N

The leaf N ranged between 1.50 to 1.68 percent in the first year of investigation. Highest leaf N (1.68%) was recorded in trees sprayed with 500 ppm paclobutrazol closely followed by foliar application of 500 ppm chlormequat, foliar application of 1000 ppm paclobutrazol and 1000 ppm chlormequat registering leaf N of 1.67, 1.65 and 1.65 percent, respectively and were at par with each other. Lowest leaf N (1.50%) was recorded in untreated trees.

During second year of experimental trial, there was a non-significant effect of different treatments on leaf N and its value ranged between 1.32 to 1.48 percent. Different treatments exerted significant effect on leaf N as calculated in the pooled data, wherein highest leaf N (1.58%) was observed with foliar application of 500 ppm paclobutrazol and was at par with leaf N found with the foliar application of 500 ppm chlormequat (1.57%) and minimum leaf N (1.41%) was found in untreated trees. It is also evident from the data that there was a slight decrease in leaf N with the increasing doses of paclobutrazol and chlormequat.

4.2.8.2 Leaf P

The effect of growth retardants on total leaf P was non-significant. The data shows negligible variation in leaf P with different treatments tried in the present investigations.

4.2.8.3 Leaf K

The effect of different treatments on leaf K was non-significant during both the years of investigation and it ranged from 1.55 to 1.69 percent in the year 2008-09 and from 1.33 to 1.50 percent in the year 2009-10. However, in the pooled data the growth retardants showed significant affect wherein, highest leaf K (1.59%) was observed with foliar application of 2000 ppm chlormequat closely followed by foliar application of 1000 ppm chlormequat and 500 ppm paclobutrazol, soil application of 6 g a.i tree-1 paclobutrazol, and foliar application of 500 ppm chlormequat registering leaf K content of 1.58, 1.58, 1.57 and 1.56 percent, respectively and were at par with each other. Lowest leaf K (1.44%) was found in untreated trees.

4.2.8.4 Leaf Ca

Leaf Ca was not significantly affected by different growth retardant treatments. However, leaf Ca ranged from 1.55 to 1.59 percent during 2008-09 and from 1.32 to 1.40 percent during 2009-10. In the pooled data, highest leaf Ca (1.50) was found with foliar application of 1000 ppm paclobutrazol and lowest (1.44%) in untreated trees.

4.2.8.5 Leaf Mg

Similarly, leaf Mg was also not significantly affected by different treatments of growth retardants. During 2008-09, highest leaf Mg (0.144%) was recorded with foliar application of 2000 ppm paclobutrazol and lowest (0.133%) in untreated trees. The leaf Mg ranged from 0.112 to 0.121 percent for all the treatments tried during 2009-10 and overall there was a decrease in leaf Mg in all the treatments as compared to leaf Mg recorded in the first year of experimentation. From the pooled data, it is clear that highest leaf Mg (0.132%) was observed with foliar application of 2000 ppm paclobutrazol and lowest (0.123%) in untreated trees.

Table 18: Effect of growth retardants on total leaf N, P, K, Ca and Mg content of olive cv. Frontoio.

Treatment	N (%)			P%			K (%)			Ca (%)			Mg (%)		
	2008-09	2009-10	Pooled	2008-09	2009-10	Pooled	2008-09	2009-10	Pooled	2008-09	2009-10	Pooled	2008-09	2009-10	Pooled
T1	1.50 (1.52)	1.32 (1.52)	1.41 (1.55)	0.22 (1.11)	0.20 (1.10)	0.21 (1.10)	1.55 (1.60)	1.33 (1.53)	1.44 (1.56)	1.55 (1.60)	1.32 (1.52)	1.44 (1.56)	0.133 (1.06)	0.112 (1.05)	0.123 (1.06)
T2	1.62 (1.62)	1.43 (1.56)	1.53 (1.59)	0.23 (1.11)	0.21 (1.10)	0.22 (1.10)	1.64 (1.63)	1.41 (1.55)	1.53 (1.59)	1.58 (1.61)	1.38 (1.54)	1.48 (1.57)	0.140 (1.07)	0.117 (1.06)	0.129 (1.06)
T3	1.60 (1.61)	1.39 (1.55)	1.50 (1.58)	0.22 (1.11)	0.20 (1.10)	0.21 (1.10)	1.68 (1.64)	1.40 (1.55)	1.54 (1.59)	1.59 (1.61)	1.38 (1.54)	1.48 (1.57)	0.140 (1.07)	0.118 (1.06)	0.129 (1.06)
T4	1.56 (1.60)	1.38 (1.54)	1.47 (1.57)	0.23 (1.11)	0.20 (1.10)	0.22 (1.10)	1.68 (1.64)	1.46 (1.57)	1.57 (1.60)	1.57 (1.60)	1.37 (1.54)	1.47 (1.57)	0.141 (1.07)	0.121 (1.06)	0.131 (1.06)
T5	1.68 (1.64)	1.48 (1.57)	1.58 (1.61)	0.23 (1.11)	0.21 (1.10)	0.22 (1.10)	1.65 (1.63)	1.51 (1.58)	1.58 (1.61)	1.58 (1.61)	1.37 (1.54)	1.48 (1.57)	0.139 (1.07)	0.118 (1.06)	0.129 (1.06)
T6	1.65 (1.63)	1.44 (1.56)	1.55 (1.59)	0.23 (1.11)	0.21 (1.10)	0.22 (1.10)	1.63 (1.62)	1.43 (1.56)	1.53 (1.59)	1.59 (1.61)	1.40 (1.55)	1.50 (1.58)	0.142 (1.07)	0.120 (1.06)	0.131 (1.06)
T7	1.63 (1.62)	1.41 (1.55)	1.52 (1.59)	0.23 (1.11)	0.21 (1.10)	0.22 (1.10)	1.64 (1.62)	1.43 (1.56)	1.53 (1.59)	1.57 (1.60)	1.36 (1.53)	1.46 (1.57)	0.144 (1.07)	0.120 (1.06)	0.132 (1.06)
T8	1.67 (1.64)	1.46 (1.57)	1.57 (1.60)	0.23 (1.11)	0.20 (1.10)	0.21 (1.10)	1.65 (1.63)	1.46 (1.56)	1.56 (1.59)	1.57 (1.60)	1.37 (1.53)	1.47 (1.57)	0.142 (1.07)	0.119 (1.06)	0.131 (1.06)
T9	1.65 (1.63)	1.44 (1.56)	1.54 (1.59)	0.23 (1.11)	0.20 (1.10)	0.22 (1.10)	1.69 (1.64)	1.47 (1.57)	1.58 (1.60)	1.57 (1.60)	1.37 (1.54)	1.47 (1.57)	0.142 (1.07)	0.114 (1.06)	0.128 (1.06)
T10	1.64 (1.62)	1.43 (1.56)	1.54 (1.59)	0.23 (1.11)	0.21 (1.10)	0.22 (1.10)	1.69 (1.64)	1.50 (1.58)	1.59 (1.61)	1.58 (1.61)	1.37 (1.54)	1.47 (1.57)	0.140 (1.07)	0.116 (1.06)	0.128 (1.06)
C.D (0.05)	0.03	NS	0.02	NS	NS	NS	NS	NS	0.03	NS	NS	NS	NS	NS	NS

Figures within the parentheses are transformed means

CHAPTER 5
DISCUSSION

Olive cultivation in India is of recent origin and has not picked up the requisite pace because of unfruitfulness and low productivity encountered in this crop. The low productivity in olives is mainly the result of poor flowering, low percentage of perfect flowers, abscission of flowers and fruit-lets consequently lesser number of fruits retained to maturity. Different horticultural techniques such as foliar application of micro-nutrients, girdling, and use of growth retardants have been used for controlling growth, flowering, fruit set and yield in fruit crops including olive. Micro-nutrients (Taheri and Taliae, 2001; Pedo *et al.* 2005), girdling (Levin and Lavee, 2005), and growth retardants (Proetti and Tombesi, 1996) have been used for encountering the problem of unfruitfulness. These techniques broadly help in modifying some of the physiological processes in olive trees which stimulate a cycle of new growth all over the year and to create an equilibrium between vegetative growth and productivity as well as stimulates photosynthetic activity of leaves, increased chlorophyll and water content, and controls excessive growth. In light of the above facts, the present investigations were carried out during 2008-09 and 2009-10 at Dhramthal, District Udhampur, Jammu and Kashmir.

In this chapter, the significant findings during the course of investigation have been discussed to offer possible explanations and evidences with a view to find out the causes and effective relationship among the different treatments tried with regard to the various attributes studied and are presented as under:

5.1 EFFECT OF GIRDLING AND FOLIAR APPLICATION OF MICRO-NUTRIENTS (ZINC AND BORON) ON GROWTH AND FRUITFULNESS OF OLIVE CV. FRONTOIO

5.1.1 Growth characteristics

Girdling and foliar sprays of zinc and boron applied singly or in combination on Frontoio cultivar of olive increased the trunk circumference. In the present investigation, a progressive increase in trunk circumference of olive trees has been observed with the increasing concentration of zinc and boron applied singly or in combination with each other and these findings are in consonance with those of Banik and Sen (1997) who also reported an increase in trunk girth of Fazli mango trees with the foliar application of 0.4 per cent boric acid in combination with 0.4 per cent zinc.

Maximum shoot extension growth of 8.92 cm was recorded in olive trees in the present investigation when sprayed with 0.6% zinc sulphate in combination with 0.6% boric acid and these findings are in conformity with the results obtained by Singh *et al.* (2009). They found that interactions of zinc, at higher levels and boron either at lower or higher concentration caused significant improvement in shoot length of mango cv. Dashehari. Decrease in shoot extension growth was recorded in olive trees with girdling as compared to untreated trees of olive and is in consonance with the findings of Ungerer and Steyn (2009) and Choi *et al.* (2010) who also observed decreased shoot growth in persimmon with girdling as compared to untreated trees.

Maximum relative growth rate (RGR) was recorded in trees sprayed with 0.5% zinc sulphate in combination with 0.6% boric acid. This positive effect of boric acid and zinc sulphate on growth might be because of promoting effect of boron on cell division and elongation process and due to involvement of zinc in the formation of tryptophan, a precursor to IAA which in turn might have stimulated growth of olive trees. Hosseini *et al.* (2007) also reported synergistic effect of boron in combination with zinc on the plant growth in corn (*Zea mays* L.).

5.1.2 Leaf area, unit leaf area and specific leaf area

Leaf area increased with the increasing concentrations of zinc and boron sprays applied singly or in combination. Maximum leaf area of 4.87 cm^2 was recorded in trees sprayed with 0.5% zinc sulphate in combination with 0.6% boric acid closely followed by trees sprayed with 0.5% zinc sulphate in combination with 0.5% boric acid, 0.6% zinc sulphate and 0.5% boric acid, 0.6% zinc sulphate in combination with 0.4% boric acid and 0.6% zinc sulphate in combination with 0.6% boric acid. The results obtained in the present investigations are in line with the findings of Hamdy *et al.* (2007) who concluded that combined application of zinc, boron and magnesium was favourable in improving the leaf area of mango.

Unit leaf area is dependent on the actual leaf area measured and the effect of foliar application of zinc and boron on leaf area and unit leaf area showed similar trend whereas, specific leaf area which is dependent on actual leaf area and leaf dry weight increased with foliar application of zinc sulphate and boric acid applied singly or in combination with each other. The results obtained in the present investigation are in total agreement with the findings of Stover *et al.* (1999) who reported that dry weight of primary spur leaves in McIntosh apple trees decreased following combined application of boron and zinc and attributed the increase in leaf area and decrease in leaf dry weight thereby resulted in increase of specific leaf area.

5.1.3 Leaf water content, stomatal count and chlorophyll content

Leaf water content increased with the foliar feeding of zinc and boron applied singly and in combination with each other and can be attributed to the overall increase in growth in response to zinc and boron sprays which might have created greater demand for water by developing leaves and shoots from the soil, which improved the leaf water content as a result of uptake of more water by the leaves from the soil. The beneficial effect of zinc and boron on plant metabolism and for regulating water uptake by plants has been well documented by Nijjar (1985).

The highest number of stomata (24.54 /microscopic field) was found in trees sprayed with 0.5% zinc sulphate in combination with 0.6% boric acid as compared to untreated trees wherein, the stomatal count of 20.96/microscopic field was observed. This small increase in stomatal count might be because of the fact that both zinc and boron stimulated new vegetative growth and the new leaves contain more number of stomata as compared to the older ones.

Foliar sprays of zinc sulphate and boric acid applied singly or in combination with each other increased leaf chlorophyll content as compared to untreated trees of olive and highest leaf chlorophyll content of 1.50 mg/g was observed in the trees sprayed with 0.4% zinc sulphate in combination with 0.6% boric acid and was at par with the values recorded in trees sprayed with 0.5% zinc sulphate in combination with 0.6% boric acid (1.48 mg/g) and 0.5% zinc sulphate in combination with 0.5% boric acid (1.45 mg/g). The findings in the present study are in line with the results obtained by Keshavarz *et al.* (2011) who recorded highest chlorophyll index in Persian walnut with foliar application of 1050 mg L^{-1} zinc in combination with 174 mg L^{-1} boron. The increase in leaf chlorophyll content with foliar sprays of zinc and boron can also be attributed to the fact that zinc is part of the carbonic anhydrous enzyme, present in all the photosynthetic tissues and it is required for chlorophyll biosynthesis (Ryugo, 1988). Nitrogen and magnesium are the main constituents of chlorophyll and improved nitrogen and magnesium status of leaves in trees sprayed with zinc and boron. However, girdling exerted no significant improvement in total leaf chlorophyll in the present investigation. The lack of response to girdling in enhancing chlorophyll may be due to elevated starch level in the leaves of girdled shoots which inhibited the photosynthetic activity as reported by Proietti and Tombesi (1990) who also obtained similar results with girdling in olive cv. Leccino.

5.1.4 Flowering characteristics

Duration of flowering was significantly reduced with foliar application of zinc in combination with boron as compared to untreated trees of olive cultivar Frontoio. This reduction in duration of flowering might be because of faster pollen tube growth with application of boron in combination with zinc, which might have reduced the time required for fertilization of ovary. The present findings are in line with the results obtained by Kumar and Sen (2004) who recorded minimum days taken to first picking with application of 45 kg/ha zinc sulphate in combination with 30 kg/ha borax in okra.

Blooming intensity was increased with girdling as well as with the foliar application of zinc sulphate and boric acid, alone or in combination with each other as compared to untreated trees of olive. The increase in blooming intensity and fruit set of olive in present study might be due to apparent mobility of boron at all developing stages of olive growth and the translocation of boron to developing tissues as was also postulated by Delgado *et al.* (1994) and Perica *et al.* (2002). Increased blooming intensity with girdling obtained in the present studies is in line with the findings of Lavee *et al.* (1983) and Barut and Eris (1993) who found that girdling caused an increase in the number of inflorescences in olive.

Highest proportion of perfect flowers was recorded in trees sprayed with 0.6% zinc sulphate and 0.5% boric acid. Similar results have been reported by Negi *et al.* (2010) who observed that application of zinc sulphate in combination with boric acid enhanced percentage of hermaphrodite flowers in mango. This increase in perfect flowers might be due to re-translocation of boron from olive leaves that occur during inflorescence development (Perica *et al.*, 2002).

5.1.5 Fruiting characteristics

In the present investigation, application of zinc in combination with boron resulted in significantly higher fruit set which is in consonance with the findings of Talaie and Taheri (2001) who also found that boron and zinc sprays caused a significant increase in final fruit set of olives by decreasing the formation of shot berries and consequently the abscission of young fruits. Similar results with the application of zinc in combination with boron have been reported in almond by Sotomayor *et al.*, (2000) and Pandit *et al.* (2011)

The application of zinc sulphate in combination with boric acid resulted in significant reduction of fruit drop of olive in the present investigation and the findings are in conformity with those of Taheri and Talaie (2001) who concluded that foliar application of zinc sulphate and boric acid at 0.5%, one week before and at full bloom led to a considerable increase in fruit set and fruit retention.

Fruit yield was significantly improved with girdling as well as with foliar application of zinc sulphate and boric acid applied singly or in combination with each other. Girdling improved the proportion of perfect flowers, increased fruit set and reduced fruit drop in olive, thus resulted in better fruit yield in the present studies. Similar influence of girdling on fruit yield has been reported in olive (Hartmann, 1950; Ben-Tal and Lavee, 1984; and Levin and Lavee, 2005), and persimmon (Steyn, *et al.* 2008). Increased fruit yield with combined application of zinc and boron could be due to the role of these two elements in preventing fruitlet abscission. Talaie and Taheri (2001) also obtained highest fruit set, and final fruit harvest with the combined application of zinc and boron in olive cv. Zard. The fruit yield during the second year of investigation was considerably lower as compared to yield obtained during the first year of investigation in all the treatments tried. This might be because of biennial bearing habit of the olive trees.

5.1.6 Physical parameters of fruits

All the physical parameters of fruits *viz.*, fruit size, fruit weight and fruit volume were significantly increased with girdling as well as with foliar application of zinc sulphate and boric acid applied singly or in combination with each other. Foliar spray of 0.5% zinc sulphate and 0.5% boric acid was found to be best in enhancing all the physical parameters of olive fruits.

Positive effect of girdling on fruit size and weight has been reported in grapes (Ahmad *et al.*, 2005), in persimmon (Choi *et al.*, 2010) and in peach (Chanana and Gill, 2006). Positive effect of zinc on fruit weight, size and volume as obtained in present investigation has also been reported by many workers in different fruit crops (Singh and Rajput, 1976; Banik and Sen, 1997; Rath *et* al., 1980; Singh *et* al., 2009 in mango), (Sharma *et al.*, 2003 in kagzi lime) and (Wali *et al.*, 2005 in phalsa). Zinc is required to obtain good fruit size being the part of the carbonic anhydrous enzyme, present in the photosynthetic tissues and it is required for chlorophyll biosynthesis (Ryugo, 1988). Similarly, boron application also resulted in an increase of fruit weight, size and volume. The beneficial effect of boron on these parameters might be because of the role of boron in cell division and cell elongation. Similar findings have been reported by Rajput *et al.* (1976) and Dutta (2004) in mango; Bybordi and Malakouti (2006) in almond and Yadav *et al.* (2010) in aonla. In the present investigation, use of zinc and boron together might have acted synergistically with each other thereby improved the physical parameters of olive fruit. Similar results have been obtained by Banik and Sen (1997) who observed a significant increase in fruit weight with the application of zinc in combination with boron in mango whereas, Tariq *et al.* (2007) also obtained maximum fruit size and fruit volume with foliar spray of zinc and boron in Blood Red cultivar of sweet orange.

5.1.7 Pulp: stone ratio and oil content

The pulp: stone ratio was significantly increased with the foliar application of boric acid in combination with zinc sulphate. The results are in conformity with the findings of Hamdy *et al.* (2007) who obtained highest pulp: stone ratio in mango cv. Hindy Bisinara with foliar application of mixture containing citric acid (500 ppm), boric acid (0.025%), chelated zinc (0.05%) and magnesium sulphate (0.25%). Oil content in olive fruits increased significantly with foliar application of zinc sulphate and boric acid applied in combination with each other. Overall improvement in fruit weight, size and pulp: stone ratio in the present study might be responsible for increased oil contents in olive fruit and the results obtained are in conformity with the findings of Jordao and Lietao (1990) who reported that there was a positive correlation between the fruit Zn concentration and the weight and oil content of the olive fruit.

5.1.8   Leaf N, P, K, Ca and Mg

Leaf nitrogen and phosphorus was not affected by girdling and foliar application of zinc sulphate and boric acid applied singly or in combination in the present study. However, leaf potassium, calcium and magnesium were increased as compared to untreated trees. Foliar application of boric acid and zinc sulphate had significant effect on the concentration of nitrogen, phosphorus and potassium in leaves and fruits of olive cultivar Zard as reported by Taheri and Talaie (2001) and the results obtained in the present study are in line with their findings.

5.2 EFFECT OF GROWTH RETARDANTS (PACLOBUTRAZOL AND CHLORMEQUAT) ON GROWTH AND FRUITFULNESS OF OLIVE CV. FRONTOIO

5.2.1 Growth characteristics

In the present investigations, there was a reduction in percent increase in trunk circumference with the increasing concentration of paclobutrazol and chlormequat. Similarly, there was a progressive decrease in shoot extension growth with the increasing concentrations of both the growth retardants applied. Similar trend was observed in case of relative growth rate (RGR) with the application of paclobutrazol and chlormequat. This reduction in shoot extension growth, and relative growth rate in trees treated with growth retardants might be attributed to the fact that both cycocel and paclobutrazol might act as potential inhibitor of gibberellins biosynthesis and thus, has caused a sharp decrease in the shoot extension growth, and relative growth rate of olive trees by decreasing the rates of cell division and cell elongation. Similar observations on the effect of paclobutrazol in reducing the vegetative growth of olive trees have been reported (Antognozzi *et al.*, 1989; Lavee and Haskal, 1993; Reduction in growth with paclobutrazol has also been reported by many workers in other fruit crops (Curry and Williams, 1983; Raese and Burts, 1983; Greene, 1986; Steffens and Wang, 1986; Costa *et al.*, 1995; Singh and Chanana, 2007; Asin *et al.*, 2007).

The use of cycocel also reduced the shoot growth and relative growth rate in comparison to control, though the effect was less pronounced as compared to soil and foliar application of paclobutrazol. This reduction in shoot growth with the application of cycocel, probably occurs due to a reduction in elongation and also by lowering the rate of cell division (Rademacher, 1995). Similar reduction in vegetative growth on application of cycocel has been reported in mango (Choudhari and Rudra, 1971; Ravishankar *et al.*, 1993; Kurian and Iyer, 1993), phalsa (Chundawat and Gupta, 1974), pear (Jaumien, 1971; Singh and Sharma, 1973; Embree *et al.*, 1987), and apple (Soczek and Zaziabi, 1978; Kaplya and Pantalienko, 1981; Hircovskey and Gajdosechova, 1984 and Bliek 1985).

5.2.2 Leaf area, unit leaf area and specific leaf area

Leaf area, unit leaf area and specific leaf area reduced with the increasing concentrations of growth retardants used in the present investigation. Minimum leaf area (2.93 cm^2) was obtained with soil application of 6 g a.i tree^{-1} paclobutrazol as well as with foliar application of 2000 ppm paclobutrazol. These findings are in consonance with the results obtained by Antognozzi *et al.* (1989) who reported that out of different foliar and soil treatments with paclobutrazol, soil application reduced total leaf area in olive trees. The reduction in leaf area following PP333 treatment has also been reported by Kumar *et al.* (1998) in grapes, Chanana and Gill (2007) in peach, Kumari and Mankar (2008) in mango, Siqueira *et al.* (2008) in lemon, and Aloni *et al.* (2010) in date palm. There was a reduction in leaf area with increasing concentration of chlormequat in the present study and the results obtained are in conformity with the findings of Chundawat and Gupta (1974) who also observed a progressive reduction in leaf area with the increasing concentrations of chlormequat in phalsa. Decrease in leaf area with chlormequat has also been reported by Embree *et al.* (1987) in pear, Kurian and Iyer (1993) in mango, Ramteke and Somkumar (2005) in grapes and Sharma *et al.* (2011) in olives. Unit leaf area and specific leaf area are dependent on the actual leaf area measured hence similar response of these two parameters was observed with the application of different growth retardants as was obtained for actual leaf area.

5.2.3 Leaf water content, stomatal count and chlorophyll content

Leaf water content decreased in response to both soil and foliar application of growth retardants in the present study and the findings are in consonance with those of Sharma *et al.* (2011) who found negative leaf water potential with use of growth retardant treatments as compared to control. Though there was a decrease in stomatal count with the increasing concentrations of both paclobutrazol and cycocel, however, overall stomatal count was improved in olive trees by the use of growth retardants as compared to untreated trees. Similar observations have been made by Suryanaryan and Rao (1978) who reported that spray of chlormequat in mango reduced the number of stomata, whereas Abo-Rawash *et al.* (1991) found that increasing spray concentration of chlormequat or paclobutrazol from 500 to 1000 ppm decreased the number of stomata in fig. Significant increase in chlorophyll content was found in trees sprayed with 500 ppm chlormequat as compared to control and the results obtained in the present investigation are in consonance with those of Suryanarayana (1981) who observed that in mango cv. Mulgoa trees sprayed with chlormequat or daminozide, each at 5000 ppm, at monthly intervals between May and January, the levels of chlorophyll and carotenoids consistently increased in chlormequat treated leaves. Similar increase in leaf chlorophyll content with foliar application of chlormequat has also been reported in tea by Kathiravetpillai and Kulasegaram (1981) and in pear by Rai and Tewari (1986). There was no significant effect of soil application of paclobutrazol in increasing leaf chlorophyll content in the present investigation and the results thus obtained are in line with the findings of Navarro *et al.* (1989) who also reported that application of paclobutrazol in rooted cuttings of olive in nutrient solution did not affect the leaf chlorophyll content significantly, whereas, foliar application of paclobutrazol in the present study improved leaf chlorophyll contents as compared to untreated trees of olive and the findings are in conformity with the results of Mobli and Baninasab (2008) who also found that paclobutrazol sprayed at 500 and 1000 ppm significantly increased leaf chlorophyll content of *Prunus amygdalus* and *Prunus webbii* seedlings as compared with the untreated seedlings.

5.2.4 Flowering characteristics

The duration of flowering decreased with the increasing concentrations of paclobutrazol and chlormequat used in the present studies. Similar trends have been obtained in mango by Mouco *et al.* (2010) who reported advanced blooming by 25 days and 15 days with the use of paclobutrazol and chlormequat, respectively. There was an increase in blooming intensity with the increase in concentration of both growth retardants *viz.*, paclobutrazol and chlormequat used in the present studies.

Paclobutrazol is a known inhibitor of gibberellins synthesis and the reduced endogenous levels of gibberellins might have favoured early and profuse flowering in the present investigation. More so over the promoting effect of paclobutrazol and chlormequat on flowering might be because of distinct suppression of vegetative growth as observed in the present investigation which may have reduced competition of vegetative parts for soil moisture and nutrients as well as increased availability of metabolites to floral buds. Similar effects of paclobutrazol and chlormeqaut on flowering have been reported by Daulta *et al*. (1981), Ravishankar *et al*. (1993), Blaikie *et al* (2004) and Singh and Ranganath (2006) in mango and Sharma *et al*. (2011) in olive. The proportion of perfect flowers improved with the increasing concentrations of paclobutrazol and chlormequat. The increase in hermaphrodite flowers with the application of chlormequat in the present investigations can be supported by the findings of Daulta *et al*. (1981) in mango and Hegazi and Stino (1982) in olive who also obtained similar response with the application of chlormequat. Increase in percentage of perfect flowers with soil and foliar application of paclobutrazol has also been reported by Burondkar and Gunjate (1993), Kumari and Mankar (2008) in mango and Sharma *et al*. (2011) in olives further supports the findings of the present investigation.

5.2.5 Fruiting characteristics

Fruit set increased with the increasing concentration of growth retardants tried in the present studies. The highest fruit set was observed in trees sprayed with 1000 ppm paclobutrazol and was at par with the fruit set obtained in trees sprayed with 2000 ppm paclobutrazol whereas lowest fruit set was found in untreated trees. The present findings are in conformity with those of Saini and Sharma (2010) who obtained increased fruit set in Red Beaut cultivar of plum with foliar application of paclobutrazol and chlormequat. Chandel and Jindal (1991) also obtained increase in fruit set with increasing doses of paclobutrazol in Japanese plum. Sansavini *et al*. (1988) concluded that CCC was associated with better growth control, greater flower bud formation and heavier fruit set on William and Conference pear trees. Increasing concentrations of paclobutrazol and chlormequat significantly decreased the fruit drop as compared to untreated olive trees in the present study. Out of various concentrations of paclobutrazol and chlormequat tried, foliar application of 2000 ppm paclobutrazol was most effective in reducing fruit drop. Similar decrease in fruit drop with the application of paclobutrazol has been reported by Singh and Singh (2006) in mango whereas, Thirugnanavel *et al*. (2007) obtained higher fruit retention in acid lime trees sprayed with chlormequat. Growth retardants (paclobutrazol and cycocel) used in the present study reduced the growth of fruits which might have reduced the competitive inhibition of older fruits to younger ones. Another reason for decrease in fruit drop could be due to increase in cytokinin like activity of paclobutrazol and cycocel in the fruits, since these chemicals are reported for such effects. There was an increase in fruit yield of olive with the application of different doses of paclobutrazol and chlormequat. The highest fruit yield was observed with foliar application of 2000 ppm paclobutrazol closely followed by foliar application of 1000 ppm paclobutrazol and soil application of 6 g a.i tree^{-1} paclobutrazol whereas, lowest fruit yield was found in untreated trees. The similar increase in yield with foliar application of paclobutrazol has been reported by Negi and Sharma (2009) in peach; Burondkar *et al.* (2009) in mango as well as with soil application of paclobutrazol by Porlingis *et al.* (1999) in olive, Singh and Chanana (2007) in peach, Reddy and Kurian (2008) in mango, and Sharma *et al.* (2011) in olives. The higher fruit set and reduced fruit drop as obtained in the present investigations might be responsible for increased fruit yield of olive trees with the soil and foliar application of paclobutrazol as paclobutrazol is known to alter the source sink relations in the plant which directly or indirectly re-allocates carbohydrate resources by suppressing vegetative growth (Kurian and Iyer, 1993).

5.2.6 Physical parameters of fruit

In general, there was a reduction in fruit size with the increasing concentration of paclobutrazol and chlormequat but different concentrations of both the growth retardants recorded better fruit size as compared with control. Increase in fruit size with soil application of paclobutrazol has been reported by Mavrodiev *et al.* (1987) in nectarine cv. Independence; Gaash and David (1989) in pecan nut; Carreno *et al.* (2007) in grapes and Sharma *et al.* (2011) in olives and with foliar application of paclobutrazol by Chandel and Jindal (1991) in Japanese plum. Improvement in fruit size with the foliar application of chlormequat has also been reported in grapes by Daulta *et al.* (1981), Kumar and Singh (1984) and Ramteke and Somkumar (2005) whereas, Dutta *et al.* (2008), Agrawal and Dikshit (2010) and Sharma *et al.* (2011) obtained similar results in mango, sapota and olives, respectively and the findings of the present study are in line with their findings. In the present investigations there was a decrease in fruit weight with increasing concentration of different growth retardants and maximum fruit weight was observed with soil application of 2 g a.i tree^{-1} paclobutrazol and foliar application of 500 ppm paclobutrazol closely followed by foliar application of 500 ppm chlormequat and were at par with each other. The minimum fruit weight was obtained in untreated trees. These findings are in line with those of Kumar *et al.* (1998) who reported that foliar application of cycocel (1000 mg/litre) or paclobutrazol (250 mg/litre) applied to grape cv. Arkavati, one month after winter pruning improved bunch weight. Similar increase in fruit weight with soil application as well as foliar application of paclobutrazol has also been reported by Singh and Chanana (2007) in peach. Foliar application of chlormequat has been found to increase fruit weight in olive and these findings are in line with the results reported by Agrawal and Dikshit (2010) in sapota cv. Cricket Ball. The improvement in fruit size and weight could be attributed to increased accumulation of assimilates and further translocation of extra metabolites through better partitioning towards reproductive growth. The decrease in physical traits of fruits with increasing concentrations of paclobutrazol and chlormequat is because of the growth retarding effect of these two bio-regulators.

5.2.7 Pulp: stone ratio and oil content

In the present investigation, significantly, higher pulp: stone ratio was recorded with the foliar application of paclobutrazol and chlormequat. Increase in pulp: stone ratio with the application of chlormequat has been reported by Daulta *et al.* (1981) in mango and this increase in pulp: stone ratio might be because of the improved leaf N and K status with the application of growth retardants as compared to control as observed in the present investigation. There was an overall improvement in the oil content with the application of both growth retardants (paclobutrazol and chormequat), however, significantly higher values were recorded in trees sprayed with 500 ppm paclobutrazol and was at par with oil content obtained with soil application of 2 g a.i tree⁻¹ paclobutrazol. An improvement in pulp: stone ratio with the application of paclobutrazol and chlormequat as observed in the present investigations might be responsible for higher oil content as compared to control.

5.2.8   Leaf N, P, K, Ca and Mg

There was an increase in leaf N with the application of paclobutrazol and chlormequat as compared to control. These findings are in conformity with those of Atawia and Hassan (1995) who also reported that cycocel sprays at 1000 or 2000 ppm at full bloom increased leaf N in pears whereas, leaf content of N, Ca, Mn, Zn and B increased and P, K and Cu contents decreased with the soil and foliar application of paclobutrazol in mango as reported by Werner (1993). Leaf P, Ca and Mg were not significantly affected by application of different growth retardants in the present study. However, levels of leaf K changed with the application of different growth retardants tried. The results obtained in the present investigation are in consonance with those of Kathiravetpillai and Kulasegaram (1981) who also reported an increase in leaf N, P and K contents of tea plants with foliar application of chlormequat.

CHAPTER 6
SUMMARY AND CONCLUSION

The various horticultural practices such as girdling, foliar application of micro-nutrients, growth retardants and pruning have been used in fruit crops including olives for controlling growth and regulating physiological functions of the tree thereby enhancing yield and quality of the fruits. With this background in mind, the present investigation entitled "Response of girdling, micro-nutrients and growth retardants on olive (*Olea europea* L.) cv. Frontoio" was undertaken during 2008-09 and 2009-10 in a private orchard at Dhramthal, District Udhampur, Jammu and Kashmir. The findings clearly indicated that growth and productivity of olive cv. Frontoio was significantly influenced with foliar application of micro-nutrients *viz.*, zinc sulphate and boric acid, growth retardants in olive trees. The significant findings emanating from the present investigation are summarised below:

6.1 EFFECT OF GIRDLING AND FOLIAR APPLICATION OF MICRONUTRIENTS (ZINC AND BORON) ON GROWTH AND FRUITFULNESS OF OLIVE CV. FRONTOIO

6.1.1 Maximum shoot extension (8.92 cm) was recorded in trees sprayed with 0.6% zinc sulphate in combination with 0.6% boric acid closely followed by trees sprayed with 0.6% zinc sulphate in combination with 0.5% boric acid, 0.6% zinc sulphate in combination with 0.4% boric acid, 0.5% zinc sulphate in combination with 0.6% boric acid, 0.5% zinc sulphate in combination with 0.5% boric acid and 0.5% zinc sulphate in combination with 0.4% boric acid whereas, highest relative growth rate of 0.033 cm cm^{-1} month^{-1} in trees sprayed with 0.5% zinc sulphate in combination with 0.6% boric acid.

6.1.2 Maximum leaf area of 4.82 cm^2 was found in trees sprayed with 0.5% zinc sulphate in combination with 0.6% boric acid and was at par with leaf area observed in trees sprayed with 0.5% zinc sulphate in combination with 0.5% boric acid, 0.6% zinc sulphate and 0.5% boric acid, 0.6% zinc sulphate in combination with 0.4% boric acid and 0.6% zinc sulphate in combination with 0.6% boric acid. Highest leaf water content (56.78%) and stomatal count (24.54 number/microscopic field) was observed in trees sprayed with 0.6% zinc sulphate in combination with 0.4% boric acid and 0.5% zinc sulphate in combination with 0.6% boric acid, respectively closely followed by 0.6% zinc sulphate in combination with 0.6% boric acid, 0.5% zinc sulphate in combination with 0.6% boric acid, 0.6% zinc sulphate in combination with 0.5% boric acid, 0.5% zinc sulphate in combination with 0.5% boric acid and 0.5% zinc sulphate in combination with 0.4% boric acid whereas, highest leaf chlorophyll content of 1.50 mg/g was observed in the trees sprayed with 0.4% zinc sulphate in combination with 0.6% boric acid and was at par with the values found in trees sprayed with 0.5% zinc sulphate in combination with 0.6% boric acid (1.48 mg/g) and 0.5% zinc sulphate in combination with 0.5% boric acid (1.45 mg/g).

6.1.3 Duration of flowering lasted for 16.83 days in trees sprayed with 0.6% zinc sulphate in combination with 0.5% boric acid and 0.6% zinc sulphate in combination with 0.6% boric acid whereas it lasted for 19.17 days in untreated trees of olive.

6.1.4 Highest blooming intensity of 0.50 per cent was recorded in trees sprayed with 0.5% zinc sulphate in combination with 0.4% boric acid and the treatment combinations comprising 0.5% zinc sulphate in combination with 0.5% boric acid, 0.5% zinc sulphate in combination with 0.6% boric acid, 0.6% zinc sulphate in combination with 0.5% boric acid and 0.6% zinc sulphate in combination with 0.6% boric acid were equally effective in improving the blooming intensity in olive cv. Frontoio.

6.1.5 Foliar application of 0.6% zinc sulphate in combination with 0.5% boric acid resulted in highest percentage of perfect flowers (48.00%). The treatments comprising of 0.5% zinc sulphate in combination with 0.5% boric acid, 0.4% zinc sulphate in combination with 0.5% boric acid, 0.5% zinc sulphate in combination with 0.6% boric acid, 0.4% zinc sulphate in combination with 0.6% boric acid, 0.5% zinc sulphate in combination with 0.4% boric acid and 0.6% zinc sulphate in combination with 0.4% boric acid were equally effective in augmenting the proportion of perfect flowers in the range of 43.33 to 47.33 percent.

6.1.6 Maximum fruit set (13.08%) was obtained in trees sprayed with 0.5% zinc sulphate in combination with 0.6% boric acid closely followed by trees sprayed with 0.6% zinc sulphate in combination with 0.6% boric acid and 0.5% zinc sulphate in combination with 0.5% boric acid exhibiting fruit set of 12.95 and 12.84 percent, respectively. Foliar spray of 0.5% zinc sulphate in combination with 0.5% boric acid was most effective in minimising the fruit drop and maximising the fruit yield in olive cv. Frontoio.

6.1.7 Maximum fruit size (1.59 cm) was found in trees sprayed with 0.6% zinc sulphate in combination with 0.6% boric acid, closely followed by trees sprayed with 0.6% zinc sulphate in combination with 0.5% boric acid, 0.5% zinc sulphate in combination with 0.5% boric acid, 0.5% zinc sulphate in combination with 0.6% boric acid, and 0.6% zinc sulphate in combination with 0.4% boric acid. However, fruit weight (1.46 g) was maximum with foliar application of 0.5% zinc sulphate in combination with 0.6% boric acid which was at par with trees sprayed with 0.6% zinc sulphate in combination with 0.6% boric acid (1.45g), 0.5% zinc sulphate in combination with 0.5% boric acid (1.45g), 0.6% zinc sulphate in combination with

0.5% boric acid (1.44 g), and 0.6% zinc sulphate in combination with 0.4% boric acid (1.42g). Highest fruit volume (1.61cc) was found in trees sprayed with 0.5% zinc sulphate in combination with 0.5% boric acid and 0.6% zinc sulphate in combination with 0.5% boric acid.

6.1.8 Maximum pulp: stone ratio (2.57) was observed in trees sprayed with 0.6% zinc sulphate in combination with 0.6% boric acid closely followed by trees sprayed with 0.6% zinc sulphate in combination with 0.5% boric acid, 0.5% zinc sulphate in combination with 0.5% boric acid, 0.6% zinc sulphate in combination with 0.4% boric acid, 0.5% zinc sulphate in combination with 0.6% boric acid, and 0.5% zinc sulphate in combination with 0.4% boric acid registering pulp: stone ratio of 2.56, 2.55, 2.53, 2.50 and 2.50, respectively and were at par with each other whereas, foliar application of 0.6% zinc sulphate in combination with 0.4% boric acid resulted in significantly higher oil content of 25.62% in olive fruits.

6.1.9 Highest leaf K content of 1.74 percent was found with the application of 0.5% zinc sulphate in combination with 0.4% boric acid closely followed by trees sprayed with 0.4% zinc sulphate in combination with 0.6% boric acid (1.73%), 0.4% zinc sulphate in combination with 0.5% boric acid (1.72%), 0.4% zinc sulphate in combination with 0.4% boric acid (1.72%), 0.6% boric acid applied singly (1.72%) and 0.6% zinc sulphate in combination with 0.6% boric acid (1.72%).

6.1.10 Highest leaf Ca (1.72%) was found in the leaves of trees sprayed with 0.6% zinc sulphate in combination with 0.4% boric acid closely followed by trees sprayed with 0.5% zinc sulphate in combination with 0.5% boric acid and 0.5% zinc sulphate in combination with 0.4% boric acid, and 0.6% zinc sulphate in combination with 0.5% boric acid registering leaf Ca of 1.71, and 1.70 percent, respectively.

6.1.11 Highest leaf Mg (0.154%) was observed in trees sprayed with 0.6% zinc sulphate in combination with 0.6% boric acid closely followed by trees sprayed with 0.6% zinc sulphate in combination with 0.5% boric acid, and 0.5% zinc sulphate in combination with 0.6% boric acid registering values of 0.153, 0.151 percent, respectively.

6.2 EFFECT OF GROWTH RETARDANTS (PACLOBUTRAZOL AND CHLORMEQUAT) ON GROWTH AND FRUITFULNESS OF OLIVE CV. FRONTOIO

6.2.1 Increasing concentrations of paclobutrazol reduced growth in terms of increase in trunk circumference shoot extension growth and relative growth rate. Minimum shoot extension growth (7.65 cm) and relative growth rate (0.032 cm cm^{-1} month^{-1}) was observed in trees sprayed with 2000 ppm paclobutrazol.

6.2.2 Leaf area as well as unit leaf area was significantly reduced with soil and foliar application of paclobutrazol and foliar application of chlormequat. Minimum leaf area of 2.93 cm^2 and unit leaf area of 2.93 cm^2 was obtained with soil application of 6 g a.i tree^{-1} paclobutrazol and foliar application of 2000 ppm paclobutrazol.

6.2.3 The increasing concentrations of paclobutrazol and chlormequat decreased the leaf water content and number of stomata per microscopic field in olive trees wherein lowest leaf water content of 56.24 percent was recorded in trees sprayed with 2000 ppm chlormequat and lowest stomatal count of 20.75 number/microscopic field was obtained with soil application of 6 g a.i tree^{-1} paclobutrazol and untreated trees.

6.2.4 The highest leaf chlorophyll content of 1.42 mg/g was found in trees sprayed with 500 ppm chlormequat and was at par with the chlorophyll content observed with foliar application of 2000 ppm chlormequat and 1000 ppm chlormequat.

6.2.5 The minimum duration of flowering (16.67 days) was recorded with soil application of 6 g a.i tree^{-1} paclobutrazol whereas, highest blooming intensity (0.49%) was recorded with 2000 ppm paclobutrazol and proportion of perfect flowers was highest (37.33%) in trees sprayed with 2000 ppm paclobutrazol and 2000 chlormequat.

6.2.6 The highest fruit set (12.10%) was observed in trees sprayed with 1000 ppm paclobutrazol which was at par with the fruit set of 12.09 percent obtained in trees sprayed with 2000 ppm paclobutrazol. Trees sprayed with 2000 ppm paclobutrazol exhibited lowest fruit drop of 51.63 percent and highest fruit yield of 2.27 Kg tree^{-1} closely followed by foliar application of 1000 ppm paclobutrazol and soil application of 6 g a.i tree^{-1} paclobutrazol .

6.2.7 Maximum fruit size (1.58 cm), weight (2.28 g) and volume (2.29 cc) was observed with foliar application of 500 ppm chlormequat, soil application of 2 g a.i tree^{-1} paclobutrazol and foliar application of 500 ppm paclobutrazol and soil application of 2 g a.i tree^{-1} paclobutrazol, respectively.

6.2.8 Significantly higher pulp: stone ratio (3.66) was observed in trees sprayed with 500 ppm paclobutrazol whereas, highest oil content (25.66%) was observed with foliar application of 500 ppm paclobutrazol and was at par with oil content of 25.64 percent obtained with soil application of 2 g a.i tree^{-1} paclobutrazol.

6.2.9 Highest leaf N (1.58%) was observed with foliar application of 500 ppm paclobutrazol and was at par with leaf N of 1.57 percent calculated with the foliar application of 500 ppm chlormequat.

From the results summarized above it can be concluded that different growth characteristics were significantly improved with foliar application of 0.6% zinc sulphate in combination with 0.6% boric acid or 0.5% zinc sulphate in combination with 0.6% boric acid or 0.6% zinc sulphate in combination with 0.4% boric acid. The physiological parameters were improved with 0.6% zinc sulphate in combination with 0.4% boric acid or 0.5% zinc sulphate in combination with 0.6% boric acid or 0.4% zinc sulphate in combination with 0.6% boric acid. Consistently better fruit set, reduced fruit drop, improved fruit yield and quality was obtained with 0.5% zinc sulphate in combination with 0.5% boric acid. The oil content improved with foliar spray of 0.6% zinc sulphate in combination with 0.4% boric acid. The leaf nutrient status was better with spray of 0.5% zinc sulphate in combination with 0.4% boric acid or 0.4% zinc sulphate in combination with 0.6% boric acid or 0.5% zinc sulphate in combination with 0.5% boric acid or 0.6% zinc sulphate in combination with 0.5% boric acid or 0.5% zinc sulphate in combination with 0.6% boric acid. Similarly, growth retardants significantly affected the growth and productivity of olive in the present investigation. Foliar application of 2000 ppm paclobutrazol or soil application of 6 g a.i tree^{-1} paclobutrazol resulted in better tree growth control whereas, better flowering, fruit set, fruit yield was achieved with foliar application of 1000 ppm paclobutrazol or 2000 ppm paclobutrazol or 6 g a.i tree $^{-1}$ paclobutrazol. However, fruit size, weight, volume, pulp: stone ratio and oil content was better with 500 ppm paclobutrazol or 2 g a.i tree^{-1} paclobutrazol or 500 ppm chlormequat. Application of 500 ppm chlormequat also improved the leaf nutrient status.

Thus, it can be concluded that application of 0.5% zinc sulphate in combination with 0.5% boric acid, and 1000 ppm paclobutrazol sprayed in the first week of March and repeated 30 days after the first spray improved the fruit production of olive cv. Frontoio by 30 and 45 percent, respectively as compared to the olive trees without any treatment.

REFERENCES

Abo-Rawash, M., Behairy, Z., Maximos, S., Miqahed, H. and Bashea, R. 1991. Studies on the effect of irrigation and some growth retardants in fig transplants. 3-leaf Anatomy. *Annals Agricultural Science*, **36**(1): 193-201.

Abou-Rawash, M. El-Nasr, N.A., El-Masry, H. and Ebeed, S. 1998. Effect of post-bloom spray with some chemical substances on yield and fruit quality of Taimour mango trees. *Egyptian Journal Horticulture*, **25**(1): 71-81.

Abo-Taleb, S.A. 1998. Effect of girdling on olive trees as a partial solution to biennial bearing. *Annals Agricultural Science*, **36**(1): 497-511.

Agrawal, S. and Dikshit, S.N. 2010. Studies on the effect of plant growth regulators on qualitative characters of sapota cv. Cricket Ball. *Indian Journal of Horticulture*, **67**(2): 177-180.

Ahmad, M., Kaul, R.K.. and Kaul, B.L. 2005. Effect of girdling, thinning and GA$_3$ on fruit growth, yield, quality and shelf life of Grapes (*Vitis vinifera* L.) cv. Perlette. *Acta Horticulturae*, **696**: 309-313.

Ahmad, M., Khan, M.A., Rahman, H.U., Ahmad, N., Tariq, S. and Ramzan, A. 2011. Effect of Boron and Gibberellic Acid on growth and fruit yield of Olive cv. "Uslu". *International Journal of Biology and Biotechnology*, **8**(1): 123-126.

Almeida, F.J. 1963. Acerca del melhoramento da oliveira. *Bol. Da junta National do Ziete*, Lisbon. Cited in Table Olives: Production and Processing. A. Garrido Fernandez, M.J. Fernandez, Diez, M.R. Adams, Chapman and Hall, UK, ISBN 0412718103, pp. 13.

Aloni, D.D., Hazon, H., Edom, U., Sendelham, D., Karp, C., Pumeranc, R. and Cohen, Y. 2010. Effects of growth retardants on vegetative growth of date palms. *Acta Horticulturae*, **884**: 207-213.

Amiri, M.E., Fallahi, E. and Golchin, A. 2008. Influence of foliar and ground fertilization on yield, fruit quality, and soil, leaf, and fruit mineral nutrients in apple. *Journal of Plant Nutrition*, **31**(3): 515-525

Anez., Q. M. 2009. Paclobutrazol and ammonium and potassium thiosulphates in mango 'Haden' production. *Acta Horticulturae*, **820**: 419-423.

Anonymous. 2011. Yearly data base of Department of Horticulture, Government of Jammu and Kashmir.

Antognozzi, E and Catalano, F. 1985. The effects of treatments with exogenous growth regulators on the vegetative and reproductive activities of olive. *Annalidella - Frcolta - di - Agraria - Universita - degli - Studi - di – Perugia*, **39** : 199-206.

Antognozzi, E. and Frenguelli, G. 1989. Vegetative and productive activities, photosynthesis and carbohydrate content in olive trees treated with paclobutrazol. *Annali-della-Facolta- di-Agraria-Universita-degli-Studi-di-Perugia*, **41**: 809-825

Antognozzi, E. and Preziosi, P. 1986. Effects of paclobutrazol on nursery trees of olive. *Acta Horticulturae*, **179**(II): 583-586.

Antognozzi, E., Preziosi, P. and Romani, F. 1989. Preliminary observations on the use of paclobutrazol (PP333) on olive trees in the nursery. *Annali-dilla-Facolta-di-Agraria-Universita-degli-studi di-perugia*, **41**: 313-337.

A.O.A.C. 1980. Official Methods of Analysis of the Analytical Chemists, 13th edition (W. Horowitz, ed.). Association of Official Analytical Chemists, Washington D.C., pp. 1018.

Arnon, D.I. 1949. Copper enzymes in isolated chloroplasts. Polyphenoloxidase in *Beta vulgaris*. *Plant Physiology*, **24**: 1-15.

Arora, R.K. and Yamdagni, R. 1986. Effect of different doses of nitrogen and zinc sprays on flowering, fruit set and final fruit retention in sweet lime (*C. limettioides* Tanaka.). *Haryana Agricultural University Journal of Research*, **16**(3): 233-239.

Arumugam, R. and Madhavrao, V.N. 1973. Note on the effect of growth retardants on pollen production and fruit set in grapes. *Indian Journal Agricultural Science*, **34** (6): 610-612.

Arzani, K., Bahadori, F. and Piri, S. 2009. Paclobutrazol reduces vegetative growth and enhances flowering and fruiting of mature 'J.H. Hale' and 'Red Skin' peach trees. *Horticulture Environment and Biotechnology*, **50**(2): 84-93.

Asin, L., Alegre, S. and Montserrat, R. 2007. Effect of paclobutrazol, prohexadione-Ca, deficit irrigation, summer pruning and root pruning on shoot growth, yield, and return bloom, in a 'Blanquilla' pear orchard. *Scientia Horticulturae*, **113**: 142-148.

Atawia, A. A. R. and Hasan, A. K. 1995. Effect of Alar and cycocel sprays on "Le Conte" pear trees, tree growth, flowering and leaf mineral content. *Annals of Agricultural Science,* Cairo, **40**(2): 799-809.

Babu, K.D., Dubey, A.K., and Yadav, D.S. 2007. Effect of micro-nutrients on enhancing the productivity and quality of Kinnow mandarin. *Indian Journal Horticulture,* **64**(3): 353-356.

Bajwa, G.S. 1979. Effect of Cycocel on flower bud formation and fruit set in Thompson Seedless grapevines. *Research Bullettin Marathwada Agriculture University*, **3**(11): 146-148

Bajwa, M.S., Singh, S.N. and Deol, S.S. 1977. Effect of cycocel, gibberellic acid and 4-chlorophenoxy acetic acid on the berry setting, bunch and berry size and quality in Himrod grapes. *Viticulture in Tropics*, HSI, Bangalore, pp. 258-262

Banik, B. C. and Sen, S. K. 1997. Effect of three level of iron, boron, zinc and their interactions on growth, flowering and yield of mango cv. Fazli. *The Horticulture Journal*, **10**(1): 23-29

Banik, B.C., Sen, S.K. and Bose, T.K. 1997. Effect of zinc, iron and boron in combination with urea on growth, flowering, fruiting and fruit quality of mango cv Fazli. *Environment and Ecology*, **15**(1): 122-125

Barut, E. and Eris, A. 1993. Research on the effects of girdling, thinning and plant growth regulators on yield, quality and alternate bearing in olive cv. Gemlik. *Doga Turk Tarm ve Ormanclk Dergisi*, **17**(4): 953-970

Banik, B.C. and Sen, S.K. 1997. Effect of three levels of zinc, iron, boron and their interactions on growth, flowering and yield of mango cv. Fazli. The *Horticulture Journal*, **10**(1): 23-29.

Banik, B. C., Sen, S. K. and Bose, T. K. 1999. Effect of zinc, iron and boron in combination with urea in growth, floweing, fruiting and fruit quality of mango cv. Fazli. *Environment and Ecology*, **15** (1): 122-125.

Beakbane A B and Majumdar P K. 1975. A relationship between stomatal density and growth potential in apple rootstock. *Journal of Horticultural Sciences* **50**: 285-289.

Bedford, D.O. and Pickering, S. 1919. Science and Fruit Growing. Macmillan and Company, Ltd., London.

Ben, J. and Kropp, K. 1986. Effect of CCC and Alar on the chemical composition and storage quality of Jonathan apples. *Acta Horticulturae*, **179**: 825-826.

Ben-Tal, Y. and Lavee, S. 1984. Girdling olive trees, a partial solution to biennial bearing. II. The influence of consecutive mechanical girdling on flowering and yield. *Rivista Ortoflorofruitticultura Italiana*, **68**: 441-452.

Bera, P.K., Bhattacharya, A.K., Roy, G.C. and Mazumdar, B.C. 1988. Pre-harvest sprayings with solutions of urea, zinc sulphate and NAA on cashew nut trees. *Indian Biologist*, **20**(2): 27-30.

Bhowmick, N. and Banik, B.C. 2011. Influence of pre-harvest application of growth regulators and micro-nutrients on mango cv. Himsagar. *Indian Journal of Horticulture*, **68**(1): 103-107.

Bhujbal, B.G. and Chaudhari, K.G. 1972. Interaction of gibberellin and girdling on certain fruit characteristics in Thompson Seedless grape. *Research Journal of Mahatma Phule Agriculture University*, **3**(2): 126-130

Bhujbal, B.G. and Chaudhari, K.G. 1973. Yield and quality of Thompson Seedles (*Vitis vinifera* L.) as influenced by girdling and gibberellins. *Research Journal of Mahatma Phule Agriculture University*, **4**(2): 108-112.

Bhujbal, B.G. and Wavhal, K.N. 1972. Effect of cane girdling on yield and quality of grapes. *Research Journal of Mahatma Phule Agriculture University*, **3**(2): 62-63.

Bist,L.D. 1990. Influence of PP333, Alar, CCC and Promalin on macronutrient status of pear leaf. *Acta Horticulturae*, **274**: 43-50.

Blaikie, S.J., Kulkarni, V.J. and Muller, W.J. 2004. Effect of morphactin and paclobutrazol flowering treatments on shoot and root phenology in mango cv. Kensington Pride. *Scientia Horticulturae*, **101**: 51-68.

Bliek,W. V. 1985. The use of chemical growth retardants. *Fruitteelt*, **75** (18): 496.

Blinovskii, I. K., Agofonov, N. V. and Rabei, L. A. 1980. Characteristics of apple tree growth and cropping in intensive orchards in relation to the application of chlormequat. *Izvestiya-Timiryazevskoi-Sel skokhozyistvennoi-Akademii*, **2** : 105-144.

Borun, S. and Kumar, R. 2003. Effect of NAA, zinc sulphate and urea on growth and yield of litchi (*Litchi chinensis* Sonn) cv. Purbi. *Orissa Journal of Horticulture*, **31**(1): 114-118.

Brar, J.S. and Bal, J.S. 2010. Role of Paclobutrazol and Ethephon in reproductive growth of 'Allahabad Safeda' guava (*Psidium guajava* L.) plants at different spacing. *Journal of Horticultural Science*, **5**(2): 128-133.

Brown, P.H. 2001. Transient nutrient deficiencies and their impact on yield- A rationale for foliar fertilizers. *Acta Horticulturae*, **564**: 217-223.

Burondkar, M.M. and Gunjate, R.T. 1993. Control of vegetative growth and induction of regular and early cropping in 'Alphonso' mango with paclobutrazol. *Acta Horticulturae*, **341**: 206-215

Burondkar, M.M., Jadhav, B.B. and Chetti, M.B. 2009. Post-flowering morpho-physiological behavior of Alphonso mango as influenced by plant growth regulators, polyamine and nutrients under rainfed conditions. *Acta Horticulturae*, **820**: 425-432

Bybordi, A. and Malakouti, M. J. 2006. Effects of foliar applications of nitrogen, boron and zinc on fruit setting and quality of almonds. *Acta Horticulturae*, **726**: 351-357.

Cao, S.Y. and Zhang, W.Y. 1992. Effect of paclobutrazol on vegetative growth, flowering, fruiting and yield of peach. *Plant Physiology Communications*, **28**(1): 29-32.

Carreno, J., Oncina, R., Carreno, I. and Tornel, M. 2007. Effect of paclobutrazol on vegetative growth, grape quality and yield of Napoleon table grape variety. *Acta Horticulturae*, **754**: 179-182.

Castro, J. and Sotomayor, C. 1998. The influence of boron and zinc sprays at bloom time on almond fruit set. *Acta Horticulturae*, **470**: 402-405.

Chanana, Y. R. and Gill, K.S. 2006. Impact of girdling, thining and their combination on quality and maturity in Florda Prince peach. *Indian Journal of Horticulture*, **63**(1): 27-30.

Chanana, Y.R. and Gill, K.S. 2007. Effect of soil application of paclobutrazol on growth of Earli Grande peach trees. *Indian Journal of Horticulture*, **64**(2): 211-212.

Chandel, J.S. and Jindal, K.K. 1991. Effect of triacontanol (TRIA) and paclobutrazol (PP333) on fruit set, yield and quality of Japanese plum (*Prunus salicina* Lindl.). *The Horticulture Journal*, **4**(1): 21-25.

Chaplin, M. H., Stebbins, R. L. and Westwood, M. N. 1977. Effects of fall applied boron sprays on fruit set and yield of Italian prune (*Prunus domestica* L.). *HortScience*, **12**: 500-501.

Chapman, H.D. 1964. Suggested foliar sampling and handling techniques for determining nutrient status of some field, horticultural and plantation crops. *Indian Journal of Horticulture*, **21**: 98-119.

Chen, D. M., Shen, D.X. and Li, Z. 1995. Effects of PP333 on early flowering of peach seedlings. *Acta Agriculturae – Zhejiangensis*, **7**(1): 20-23.

Chitu, V., Chitu, E. and Braniste, N. 2008. Effects of GA$_3$ and paclobutrazol treatment on fruit set and yield of 'Beurre Bosc' and 'Triumf' pears cultivars. *Acta Horticulturae*, **800**: 163-168.

Chitu, V., Butac, M., Chitu, E. and Nicolae, S. 2009. Effect of growth retardants treatment on plum yield and fruit quality. *Lucrari Stiintifice Universitatea-de-Stiinte Agronomice-si-Medicina Veterinara Bucuresti Seria-B, Horticultura*, **53**: 433-436.

Choudhari, J.M. and Rudra, P. 1971. Physiological studies on chemical control of growth and flowering in mango (*Mangifera indica* L.). *Indian Agriculturist*, **15** (1&2): 127-135.

Choi, S.T., Song, W.D., Park, D.S., and Kang, S.M. 2010. Effect of different girdling dates on tree growth, fruit characteristics and reserve accumulation in a late-maturing persimmon. *Scientia Horticulturae*, **126**: 152-155.

Chundawat, B. S. and Gupta, O. P. 1974. Effects of growth retardants (B-9 and cycocel) on vegetative growth and yield of phalsa (*Grewia asiatica* L.). *Haryana Journal of Horticultural Science*, **3**(3-4): 113-115.

Chusri, O., Kozai, N., Ogata, T., Higuchi, H. and Yonemoto, Y. 2008. Application of paclobutrazol for flowering and fruit production of 'Irwin' mango (Mangifera indica L.) in Okinawa. *Tropical Agriculture and Development*, **52**(3): 69-73.

Cimato, A. and Bartolini, G. 1987. A Handbook of Olive Cultivation.

Coetzer, L.A., Robbertse, P.J. and Wet, E-de. 1991. The influence of boron applications on fruit production and cold storage of mangoes. Yearbook South African Mango Growers' Association, **11**: 29-31.

Coombe, B.G. 1965. Increase in fruit set of *Vitis vinifera* by treatment with growth retardants. *Nature* (London), **205**: 305-306.

Costa, J. Bosch, M. and Blanco, A. 1995. Growth and cropping of 'Blanquilla' pear trees treated with paclobutrazol. *Journal of Horticultural Sciences*, **70**(3): 433-443.

Costa, C., Biasi, R., Ramina, A. and Tonutti, P. 1986. Effect of paclobutrazol soil applications on growth and fruiting of nectarine (cv. Independence). *Acta Horticulturae*, **179**: 567-570.

Cruz, M-do. C.M-da., Siqueira, D.L-de, Salomao, L.C.C. and Cecon, P.R. 2009. Flowering of the acid lime tree 'Tahiti' submitted to water stress and treated with paclobutrazol. *Cientifica Jaboticabal*, **37**(2): 53-60.

Curry, E.A. and Williams, M.W. 1983. Promalin or GA$_3$ increase pedicel and fruit length and leaf size of Delicious apples treated with paclobutrazol. *Horticultural Science*, **18**: 214-215.

Curry, E.A. and Williams, M.W. 1986. Effect of paclobutrazol on fruit quality: apple, pear and cherry. *Acta Horticulturae*, **179**: 743-753.

Daulta, B. S., Singh, H. K. and Chauhan, K. S. 1981. Effect of zinc and CCC sprays on flowering and physico chemical composition of fruit in mango (*Mangifera indica* L.) cv. Dashehari. *Haryana Journal of Horticultural Science*, **10**(3-4): 161-165.

Delgado, A., Benlloch, M. and Fernandez-Escobar, R. 1994. Mobilization of boron in olive trees during flowering and fruit development. *Horticultural Science*, **29**(6): 616-618.

Desai, U.T. Choudhari, K.G., Rane, S.D. and Patil, Y.S. 1982. Alteration of flowering period in kaghzi lime with plant growth substances. *Journal of Maharashtra Agricultural Universities*, **7**(2): 161-162.

Desouky, I.M., Haggag, L.F., El-Migeed, M.M.M.A., Kishk, Y.F.M. and El-Hady, E.S. 2009. Effect of boron and calcium nutrients sprays on fruit set, oil content and oil quality of some olive oil cultivars. *World Journal of Agricultural Sciences*, **5**(2): 180-185.

Dhillon, B.S. and Sharma, K.K. 1973. Regulation of Perlette grapes with CCC, GA 2,4,5-T and NAA. *Journal of Research Punjab Agricultural University, Ludhiana*, **10**(3): 331-336.

Dixon, B., Sagar, G. R. and Shorrsocks, V. M. 1973. Effect of calcium and boron on the incidence of tree and storage pit in apples of the cv. Egremont Russet. *Journal of Horticultural Science*, **48**: 403-411.

Dutta, P. 2004. Effect of foliar boron application on panicle growth, fruit retention and physico-chemical characters of mango cv. Himsagar. *Indian Journal of Horticulture*, **61**(3): 265-266.

Dutta, P., Banik, A. and Dhua, R. S. 2000. Effect of boron on fruit set, fruit retention and fruit quality of litchi cv. Bombai. *Indian Journal of Horticulture*, **57**(4): 287-290.

Dutta, P., Kundu, S. and Ahmed, B. 2008. Effect of plant bio-regulators on fruit quality and mineral composition of ripe mango cv. Himsagar. *Indian Agriculturist*, **52**(3/4): 107-111

Ebeed, S., El-Gazzar, A., and Bedier, R. 2001. Effect of foliar application of some micronutrients and growth regulators on fruit drop, yield, fruit quality and leaf mineral content of Mesk mango cv. trees. *Annals of Agricultural Science, Moshtohor*, **39**(2): 1279-1296.

El-Saida, S.A.G . 2001. Effect of some growth regulators and zinc sulphate treatments on yield and fruit quality of Washington Navel orange. *Annals Agricultural Science, Moshtohor*, **39**(2): 1199-1212.

Eman, A.A.A.E., El-Migeed, M.M.M.A., Omayma, M.M.I. 2007. GA $_3$ and zinc sprays for improving yield and fruit quality of Washington navel orange trees grown under sandy soil conditions. *Research Journal of Agriculture and Biological Science*, **3**(5): 498-503.

Embree, C. G., Craig, W. E. and Forsyth, F. R. 1987. Effect of daminozide, Chlormequat and paclobutrazol on growth and fruiting of "Clapp's Favorite" pears. *HortScience*, **22**(1): 55-56.

Erez, A. 1984. Dwarfing peaches by pruning and paclobutrazol. *Acta Horticulturae*, **146** : 235-241.

Faizan, A., Ather, M. and Kumar, G. 2000. Effect of paclobutrazol on growth, yield and quality of litchi (*Litchi chinensis*). *Indian Journal of Horticulture*, **57**(4): 291-294.

Farmahan, H.L. 1971. Effect of para-chlorophenoxy acetic acid, gibberellic acid and 2-chloroethyltrimethyl ammonium chloride on fruit set and development in vinifera grapes. M. Sc. Thesis, Punjab Agricultural University, Ludhiana.

FAO. 2012. Statistical Year Book 2012. A Publication of Food and Agricultural Organization. Available at *http://faostat3.fao.org /home /index.html# DOWNLOAD*

Fontanazza, G., Rugini, E. and Baldoni, L. 1987. The effect of SADH (succinic acid 2, 2-dimethylhydrazide), shoot-tying, girdling and pruning on fruiting of the olive tree 'Ascolana Tenera'. *Olea*, **18**: 43-47.

Forlani, M. and Rotundo, A. 1974. The use of cycocel (chlormequat) on olive. *Annali della Facolta di Scienze Agrurie della Universita degli Studi di Napoli, Portici*, **8**: 1-8.

Gaash, D. and David, I. 1989. Paclobutrazol effect on growth and cropping of pecan trees. *Acta Horticulturae*, **239**: 301-304.

Gaash, D., David, I. and Ran, I. 1989. Plum high density planting - 10 year trials. *Acta Horticulturae*, 243: 331-335.

Garg, R. C. and Singh, S. K. 1970. Effect of ethrel and cycocel on growth, flowering, fruiting behaviour and yield of cape goose berry (*Physalis pervuviana*L.). *Progressive Horticulture*, **8**(3): 45-50.

Goguey, T. 1992. The cumulative effects of cultar (paclobutrazol) on volencia mango. *Fruits-Paris*, **47**(1): 55-63.

Gonzalez, C., Zheng, Y. and Lovatt, C.J. 2010. Properly timed foliar fertilization can and should result in a yield benefit and net increase in grower income. *Acta Horticulturae*, **868**: 273-285.

Goren, R., Huberman, M. and Goldschmidt, E.E. 2004. Girdling: Physiological and horticultural aspects. *Horticultural Reviews*, **30**: 1-36.

Grauslund, J. 1974. The effects of SADH and chlormequat on young pear trees. *Frugtavteren*, **3**(10): 398-400.

Grauslund, I. 1983. Growth retardation in pear trees using cycocel. *Medddelelse-Statens-Planteavlsforsog*, 85(1717): 4.

Greene, D. W. 1986. Effect of paclobutrazol and analogs on growth, yield, fruit quality and storage potential of Delicious apples. *Journal of the American Society for Horticultural Science*, **111**: 328-332.

Grierson, W., Soule, J., and Kawada, K. 1982. Beneficial aspects of physiological stress. *Horticultural Reviews*, **4**: 247-271.

Griggs, W.H. and Iwakiri, B.T. 1975. Pollen tube growth in almond flowers. *California Agriculture*, **25(7)**: 4-7.

Gu, M.R., Jiang, Y.M., Hang, H.C. and Peng, F.T. 1995. Translocation and distribution of boron in apple trees foliar applied at flowering. *Acta Agriculturae Nucleatae-Sinica*, **9**(2): 86-90.

Guha, D. 1993. Regulation of tree growth and yield in Golden Delicious apple with cycocel and ethrel. *South Indian Horticulture*, **41**(6): 333-340.

Haggag, L.F., Maksoud, M.A. and El-Barkouky, F.M.Z. 1995. Effect of boron sprays on sex ratios and fruit quality of mango (*Mangifera indica* L.) cv. Hindi Be-Sinnara. *Annals of Agricultural Science*, Cairo, **40**(2): 753-758.

Hamdy, I. M. I., Ahmed, Y. M., Ahmed, F.F. 2007. Relation of fruiting in Hindy Bisinara mangoes to foliar nutrition with Mg, B and Zn and some antioxidants. In: 8th African Crop Science Society Conference, El-Minia, Egypt, 27-31 October, 2007, p. 411-415.

Hansen, P. 1981. Boron toxicity and bud development in apple trees. *Tidsskrift for Planteavl*, **85**(4): 405-410.

Hanson, E. J. 1991. Sour cherry trees respond to foliar boron application. *Horticultural Science*, **26**(9): 1142-1145.

Hao, S.Q., Yang, H. and Sun, Z.M. 1991. Effects of PP333 on the growth and fruiting of young 'Delicious' apple trees. *Acta Horticulturae Sinica*, **18**(4): 318-322.

Hartmann, H.T. 1950. The effect of girdling on flower type, fruit set, and yields in the olive. *Proceedings of the American Society for Horticultural Science*, **56**: 217-226.

Hartmann, H.T. 1953. Effect of winter chilling on fruitfulness and vegetative growth in the olive. *Proceedings of the American Society for Horticultural Science*, **62**: 184-186.

Hegazi, E. S. and Stino, G. R. 1982. Chemical regulation of sex expression in certain olive cultivars. *Acta Agrobotanica*, **35**(2): 185-190.

Helail, B.M. and Eissa, M.A. 1997. Effect of some cultural practices and growth regulator treatments on growth of mango seedlings. *Annals of Agricultural Science, Moshtohor*, **35**(2): 883-894.

Hircovsky, E. and Gajdosechova, E. 1984. Effect of the morphoregulators, Alar 85 and Ratacel on the growth and yield potential of selected apple cultivars. *Vedecke-Pruce-Vyskumneho-Ustava-Ovocnyeh-a-Okrasnych Drevin V. Bojniciach*, **5**: 181-192.

Hoda, M. N., Singh, J. and Singh J. 2001. Effect of cultar on flowering, fruiting and fruit quality of mango cv. Langra. *Indian Journal of Horticulture*, **58**(3): 224-227.

Hosseini, S.M., Maftoun, M., Karimian, N., Ronaghi, A. and Emam, Y. 2007. Effect of zinc x boron interaction on plant growth and tissue nutrient concentration of corn. *Journal of Plant Nutrition*, **30**(5): 773-781.

Hricovsky, I. 1978. Application of alar 85 and cycocel on apples in Czechoslovakia. *Acta Horticulturae*, **80**: 465-466.

Huang, C.F., Shu, D.L., Shu, Q.Z. and Yan, X.J. 2005. Effect of applying boron on the production of chestnut. *South China Fruits*, **5**: 72

Hu, Z., Zhang, C.M. and Wang, S.B. 1988. A preliminary report on the effect of PP333 on shoot growth and fruit setting of orange. *Shanxi Fruit Trees*, **2**: 30-31

Jackson, M.L. 1973. Soil Chemical Analysis. Prentice Hall of India Ltd., New Delhi, pp. 498.

Jacyna, T. 2007. Effects of paclobutrazol applied to tree bark on performance of sweet cherry and apparent soil residue. *Journal of Horticultural Science and Biotechnology*, **82**(1): 19-24.

Jain, M.C. and Dashora, L.K. 2007. Growth, flowering, fruiting and yield of guava (*Psidium guajava* L.) cv. Sardar as influenced by various plant growth regulators. *International Journal of Agricultural Sciences*, **3**(1): 4-7.

Jaumien, F. 1971. The effect of CCC on the growth and cropping of young Doyenne du Comice pears in the year of treatment and the subsequent years. *Acta Agrobotanica*, **24**(1): 63-85.

Jiang, C.C., Wang, Y.H., Liu, G.D. Xia, Y., Peng, S., Zhong, B.L. and Zeng, Q.L. 2009. Effect of boron on the leaf etiolation and fruit drop of Newhall Navel orange in southern Jiangxi. *Plant Nutrition and Fertilizer Sciences*, **15**(3): 656-611.

Jones, K.M., Bound, S.A., Koen, T.B. and Oakford, M.J. 1991. Improving fruit set on young red 'Delicious' apple trees using autumn sprays of paclobutrazol and ethephon. *Journal of Horticultural Sciences*, **66**(2): 165-169.

Jordao, P.V. and Lietao, F. 1990. The olive mineral composition and some parameters of quality in fifty olive cultivars in Portugal. *Acta Horticulturae*, **286**: 461-464.

Jovanovic, M. 1972. The effect of boron and manganese nutrition on the properties of Golden Delicious apple fruits. *Zbornik Radova Poljoprivrednog Faculteta*, **20**(540): 1-56.

Kangarshahi, A.A., Amiri, N.A., Malakouti, M.J. and Moradi, B. 2007. Effect of rates and methods of zinc application on yield and fruit quality of Satsuma Mandarin. *Iranian Journal of Soil and Water Science*, **21**(1): 1- 4.

Kaplya, A. V. and Pantalienko, A. V. 1981. Effect of chlormequat on the content of tree amino acids in apple roots. *Visnik kiiv Un-tu Biot.*, **23**: 5-9.

Karuna, K. and Mankar, A. 2008. Effect of urea, paclobutrazol and bio-regulators on vegetative growth and productivity of Langra mango. *The Orissa Journal of Horticulture*, **36**(2): 88-92.

Kathiravetpillai, A. and Kulasegaram, S. 1981. Effects of (2-chloroethyl) trimethyl-ammonium chloride (CCC) on growth and of gibberellic acid (GA$_3$) and CCC on chlorophyll and NPK content of leaves of young tea plants. *Tea Quarterly*, **50**(2): 84-94.

Kenworthy, A.L. 1964. Fruit, nut and plantation crops, deciduous and evergreen. A guide for collecting foliar samples for nutrient element analysis. *Memo Horticultural Department* Michigan State University, Michigan, pp. 223-24.

Keshavarz, K., Vahdati, K., Samar, M., Azadegan, B. and Brown, P.H. 2011. Foliar application of zinc and boron improves walnut vegetative and reproductive growth. *HortTechnology*, **21**(2): 181-186.

Khader, S. A. and Rao, V.N.M. 1984. Studies on chemical control of flowering in grapevine. II. Effect on flowering and related characters. *South Indian Horticulture*, **32**(1): 1-15.

Khader, S.A. 1991. Control of tree height, trunk girth, shoot growth and total assimilation in young grafted mango trees by paclobutrazol. *Indian Journal of Horticulture*, **48**(2): 112-115.

Khader, S. A., Pal, R. N. and Srivastava, K. C. 1989. Studies on delaying panicle expansion and flowering by growth retardants in mango. *Acta Horticulurae,* **231**: 412-423.

Khafagy, S.A.A., Zaied, N.S., Nageib, M.M., Saleh, M.A., and Fouad, A.A. 2010. The beneficial effects of yeast and zinc sulphate on yield and fruit quality of Navel orange trees. *World Journal of Agricultural Sciences*, **6**(6): 635-638.

Khalifa, R.K.M., Omaima, M.H. and Abd-El-Khair, H. 2009. Influence of foliar spraying with boron and calcium on productivity, fruit quality, nutritional status and controlling of blossom end rot disease of Anna apple trees. *World Journal of Agricultural Sciences*, **5**(2): 237-249.

Kilany, O.A., Gamal, N.W. and Kilany, A.S. 1986. Effect of some growth regulators on fruit set and quality of "Ghariby" grape. *Annals of Agricultural Science,* Moshtohor, **24**(4): 2189-2198.

*Kilany, A. E. and Kilany, O. A. 1991. Effect of potassium and boron nutrients on growth, yield and fruit quality of Anna apple trees. *Bulletin of Faculty of Agriculture University of Cairo*, **42**(2): 415-428.

Koodziejczak, P. and Tymoszuk, S. 1992. The effect of Cultar on growth and yield of Stanley plum. *Fruit Science Reports*, **19**(1): 19-24.

Kovaleva, A.F. and Cherevko, A.I. 1986. Effect of retardants on the growth and productivity of young pear trees. *Sbornik Nauchnykh Trudov, Vsesoyuznyi Nauchno Issledovatel'ski Institut Sadovodstva zimeni IV Michurina*, **46**: 57-58.

Kumbhar, A.R., Gunjate, R.T., Thimaiah, I.M. and S.M. Amin. 2009. Comparison of cultar and austar as source of paclobutrazol for flowering and fruiting in Kesar mango. *Acta Horticulturae*, **820**: 403-405.

Kumari, K. and Mankar, A. 2008. Effect of urea, paclobutrazol and bio-regulators on vegetative growth and productivity of Langra mango. *The Orissa Journal of Horticulture*, **36**(2): 88-92./

Kumar, H. and Singh, I.J. 1984. Effect of cycocel on floral drop, growth and fruit quality in grape (*Vitis vinifera* L.) cv. Thompson Seedless. *Haryana Journal of Horticultural Science*, **13**(3/4): 106-109.

Kumar, M. and Sen, N.L. 2004. Interaction effect of zinc and boron on okra (*Abelmoschus esculentus* L. Moench) cv. Prabhani Kranti. *Agricultural Science Digest*, **24**(4): 307-308.

Kumar, R., Kumar, P. and Singh, U.P. 2008. Effect of foliar application of nitrogen, zinc and boron on flowering and fruiting of mango (*Mangifera indica* L.) cv Amrapali. *Environment and Ecology*, **26**(4B): 1965-1967.

Kumar, R., Rai, R.M. Singh, R.B. and Pant, N. 2005. Effect of growth retardants on vegetative growth, yield and fruit quality of high density peach trees. *Journal of Applied Horticulture*, **7**(2): 139-141.

*Kumar, A.K., Murti, G.S.R. and Shikhamany, S.D. 1998. Effect of cycocel and paclobutrazol on morphological attributes, bunch characteristics, and endogenous gibberellin levels in 'Arkavati' grape (*Vitis vinifera* L.) trained on two systems. *Gartenbauwissenschaft*, **63**(2): 63-65.

Kurian,R.M. and Iyer,C.P.A. 1993. Chemical regulation of tree size in mango (*Mangifera indica* L.) cv. Alphonso. III. Effects of growth retardants on yield and quality of fruits. *Journal of Horticultural Science*, **68**(3): 361-364.

Lal, B., Malhi C.S. and Singh, Z. 1998. Effect of foliar and soil applications of zinc sulphate on zinc uptake, tree size, yield, and fruit quality of mango. *Journal of Plant Nutrition*, **21**(3): 589-600.

Lavee, S. 1989. Involvement of plant growth regulators and endogenous growth substances in the control of alternate bearing. *Acta Horticulturae*, **239**: 311-322.

Lavee, S.; Haskal, A. and Ben-Tal, Y. 1983. Girdling olive trees, a partial solution to biennial bearing. I. Methods, timing and direct tree response. *Journal of Horticultural Science*, **58**: 209-218.

Lavee, S. and Haskal, A. 1993. Partial fruiting regulation of olive trees (*Olea europaea* L.) with paclobutrazol and gibberellic acid in the orchard. *Advances in Horticultural Science*, **7**(2): 83-86.

Levin, A.G. and Lavee, S. 2005. The influence of girdling on flower type, number, inflorescence density, fruit set and yields in three different olive cultivars (Bernea, Picual, and Souri). *Australian Journal of Agricultural Research*, **56**: 827-831.

Ljubkin, Ju. I. 1969. The effect of boron on bearing apple orchards Ref. Z. 4.55.540.

Lone, I.A. 2007. Combined effect of soil and foliar application of boron and calcium on yield and quality of apple cv. Red Delicious. *Asian Journal of Soil Science*, **2**(1): 40-42.

Lopez, R.E.P. and Suarez, G.M.P. 1990. Olive tree girdling: optimum timing and widths. *Olivae*, **32**: 38-41

Lovatt, C. 1991. Factors affecting fruit set / early drop in avocado California Avocado Society Yearbook, **75**: 193-199.

Luckwill, L. C. 1970. The control of growth and fruitfulness of apple trees. In: *Physiology of Tree Crops*, 237-254.

Mahalle, S.S., Ingle, H.V. and Sable, P.B. 2010. Influence of plant growth regulators and chemicals on yield and quality of Hasta bahar in acid lime. *Green Farming*, **1**(3): 285-287.

Maiti, S.C., Basu, R.N. and Sen, P.K. 1972. Chemical control of growth and flowering in *Mangifera indica* L. *Acta Horticulturae*, **24**:194-197.

Maksoud, M. A., Amera, A. F., Fekrya, H. K. and Lailia, F. H. 2004. Effect of boron fertilization on growth, yield and fruit quality of olives. *Arab Universities Journal of Agricultural Sciences*, **12**(1): 361-369.

Malstrom, H.L., Fenn, L.B., and Riley, T.R. 1984. Methods of zinc fertilization. *Pecan South*, **11**(3): 16-19.

Mansour, N. M. and El-Sied, Z. 1981. Effect of zinc sulphate on fruit set and yield of guava trees. *Agricultural Research Review*, **59**(3): 119-135.

Martin, G.C., Yoshikawa, F. and LaRue, J.H. 1987. Effect of soil applications of paclobutrazol on vegetative growth, pruning time, flowering, yield, and quality of 'Flavorcrest' peach. *Journal of the American Society for Horticultural Science*, **112**(6): 915-921.

Mavrodiev, S., Kolev, K. and Manolov, P. 1987. Effects of cultar on growth and fruiting of peach. *Proc. IV International Symposium on Plant Growth Regulators*, **2**: 928-932.

Menzel, C. M. and Simpson, D. R. 1990. Effect of paclobutrazol on growth and flowering of lychee (*Litchi chinensis*). *Australian Journal of Experimental Agriculture*, **30**: 131-137.

Merwin, A. and Peech, J. 1951. Soil analysis. *Soil Science Society of America Proceedings*, **15**: 125-28.

Miller, S.S. and Tworkoski, T. 2003. Regulating vegetative growth in deciduous fruit trees. Quarterly reports on plant growth regulation and activities of The Plant Growth Regulation Society of America, **31**: 8-46.

Mobli, M. and Baninasab, B. 2008. Effects of plant growth regulators on growth and carbohydrate accumulation in shoots and roots of two almond rootstock seedlings. *Fruits Paris*, **63**(6): 363-370.

Mohammad, A.A., Hassan, J.A. and Poulis, A.T. 1987. Effect of CCC on fruit set and yield of Roomy Red grape cultivar. *The Iraqi Journal of Agricultural Sciences*, **5**(4): 41-45.

Mouco, M.A.do C., Ono, E.O. and Rodrigues, J.D. 2010. Mango flower induction in the Brazilian Northeast semi-arid with gibberellins synthesis inhibitors. *Acta Horticulturae*, **884**: 591-596.

Muhammad, S., Abdur, R., Nawab, A., Muhammad, A., Ferguson, L. and Masood, A. 2010. Effect of foliar application of Zn and B on fruit production and physiological disorders in sweet orange cv. Blood orange. *Sarhad Journal of Agriculture*, **26**(3): 355-360.

Mukhopadhyay, A.K. 1976. A note on the effect of growth retardants and L-methionine on flowering of mango (*Mangifera indica* L). *Haryana Journal of Horticultural Sciences*, **5**(3/4): 169-171.

Nambisan, J.V., Desai, U.T., Kshirsagar, D.B. and Kamble, A.B. 2007. Effect of plant growth regulators on yield of sapota cv. Kalipatti. *Journal of Maharashtra Agricultural Universities*, **32**(2): 280-281.

Navarro, C., Benlloch, M. and Escobar, R.F. 1989. Effect of paclobutrazol on growth of rooted olive cuttings. *Acta Horticulturae*. **239**: 265-268.

Negi, N.D. and Sharma, N. 2009. Effect of paclobutrazol application and planting systems on growth and production of peach (*Prunus persica*). *Indian Journal of Agricultural Sciences*, **79**(12): 1010-1012.

Negi, S.S., Singh, A.K. and Rai, P.N. 2010. Effect of foliar application of nutrients on pollen, flowering, fruit set, fruit drop and yield in mango cv. Dashehari. *The Horticulture Journal*, **23**(2): 45-48.

Nicotra, A. 1979. The effects of Cycocel on pear. *Annali dell' Istituto Sperimentale per la Frutticoltura.*, **10**: 59-68.

Nicotra, A., Damiano, C., Moser, L. and Malagodi, G. 1977. Effect of cycocel spray on Doyenne du Comice pear variety. *Acta Horticulturae*, **69**: 201-208.

Nijjar, G.S. 1985. Nutrition of Fruit Trees. Mrs. Usha Raj Kumar Kalayan, New Delhi, pp 70-119.

Noel, A.R.A. 1970. The girdled tree. *Botanical Reviews*, **36**: 162-195.

Nyomora, A.M.S., Brown, P.H. and Freeman, M. 1997. Fall foliar applied boron increases tissue boron concentration and nut set of almond. *Journal of the American Society for Horticultural Science*, **122**(3): 405-410.

Nyomora, A.M.S., Brown, P.H. and Krueger, B. 1999. Rate and time of boron application increase almond productivity and tissue boron concentration. *HortScience*, **34**(2): 242-245.

Omaima, M.H. and El-Metwally, I.M . 2007. Efficiency of zinc and potassium sprays alone or in combination with some weed control treatments on weeds growth, yield and fruit quality of Washington Navel orange orchards. *Journal of Applied Sciences Research*, **July**: 613-621.

Palese, A.M. and Crocker, S.J. 2002. Preliminary investigations of endogenous gibberellins in seeds of olive fruits. *Acta Horticulturae*, **586**: 525-528.

Pandit, A.H., Wani, M.S., Mir, M.A., Bhat, K.M., Wani, S.M. and Malik, A.R. 2011. Effect of foliar application of boron and zinc on fruit set and productivity of almond. *Acta Horticulturae*, **903**: 1007-1009.

Pan, J. P., Li, J. G., Yang, B. M. and Li, J. S. 1995. Influence of PP333 on growth of loquat tree. *Guangdong Agricultural Sciences*, **1**: 28-29.

Panse, V.G. and Sukhame, P.V. 2000. Statistical methods for agricultural workers. Publication Information Division of ICAR, New Delhi.

Patel, B.M. and Patel, H.C. 1985. Effect of foliar application of zinc and iron on chlorophyll and micronutrient contents of acidlime (*Citrus aurantifolia* Swingle). *South Indian Horticulture*, **33**(1): 50-52.

Pedò, S., Failla, O., Bassi, D. and Gigliotti, C. 2005. Livelli critici di boro nelle foglie in oliveti del Nord Italia. *Inf. tore Agr*, **22**: 40-42.

Pelevina, L.V. 1980. Effect of manganese and zinc on leaf water retaining capacity and productivity of apple trees. Fiziologiya-i-Biokhimiya-Kul'-turnykh-Rastenii, **12**(3): 319-322.

Perica, S., Brown, P.H., Connell, J.H., Nyomora, M.S.A., Dordas, C., and Hu, H. 2001. Foliar Boron Application Improves Flower Fertility and Fruit Set of Olive. *HortScience*, **36**(4): 714-716.

Perica, S., Brown, P. H., Connell, J. H. and Hu, H. 2002. Olive response to foliar boron application. *Acta Horticulturae*, **586** : 381-383.

Piper, C.S. 1950. Soil and Plant Analysis. University of Adelaide, Australia, pp. 16.

Piper, C.S. 1966. Soil and Plant Analysis. Hans Publishers, Bombay, India, pp. 40-51.

Pirogova, D.M. 1979. Foliar nutrition of apple transplants with minor elements and heteroauxin.. *Vopr-Les-Biogeotsenol-Ekol-i-Okhrany-Prirody-v-Step-Zone*, **4**: 55-63.

Pons, F. 1996. Zinc is often an under-exposed element. *Fruitteelt Den Haag*, **86**(36): 14-15.

Porlingis, I. C. and Voyiatzis, D. G. 1986. Influence of paclobutrazol plant growth regulator on vegetative and reproductive growth of olive (*Olea europaea* L.). *Acta Horticulturae*, **179** : 587-588.

Porlingis, I.C. and Voyiatzis, D.G. 1999. Paclobutrazol decreases the harmful effect of high temperatures on fruit set in olive trees. *Acta Horticulturae*, **474**: 241-244.

Porlingis, I. C., Vayiatzis, D. G., Metzidakis, I. T., Voyitzis, D. G. 1999. Paclobutrazol decreases the harmful effects of high temperatures on fruit set in olive trees. *Acta Horticulturae*, **474**: 241-244.

Potopova, V.V. 1974. The effect of foliar applied microelements on apple seedling development. *Khimiya-v-Sel'-skom-Khozyaistve*, **12**(5): 18-20.

Proietti, P. and Tombesi, A.1990. Effect of girdling on photosynthetic activity in olive leaves. *Acta Horticulturae*, **286**: 215-218.

Proietti, P. and Tombesi, A. 1996. Effects of Gibberellic acid, asparagine and glutamine on flower bud induction in olive. *Journal of Horticultural Sciences*, **71**(3): 383-388.

Qin, X.N. 1996. Foliar spray of B, Zn and Mg and their effects on fruit production and quality of Jincheng orange (*Citrus sinensis*). *Journal of South-west Agricultural University*, **18**(1): 40-45.

Quinlan, J.D. 1987. Use of paclobutrazol in orchard management to improve efficiency of fruit production. Monograph-British Crop Protection Council No. **36**: 149-53.

Quinlan, J. D. and Webster, A. D. 1982. Effects of the growth retardant PP333 on the growth of plums and cherries. 21st International Horticultural Congress, Vol. I, 1071p.

Rademacher, W. 1995. Growth retardants: biochemical features and applications in horticulture. *Acta Horticulturae*, **394**: 57-73.

Rademacher, W. 2000. Growth retardants: effect on gibberellins biosynthesis and other metabolic pathways. *Annual Review of Plant Physiology and Plant Molecular Biology*, **51**: 501-531.

Raese, J.T. and Burts, E. C. 1983. Increased yield and suppression of shoot growth and mite population of "d Anjou" pear trees with nitrogen and paclobutrazol. *Horticultural Sciences*, **18**: 212-214.

Rai, R.M. and Tewari, J.D. 1986. Effect of pre-harvest sprays of growth regulators on growth and chlorophyll pigment of pear (*Pyrus communis* L.) cv. Victoria. *Progressive Horticulture*, **18**(3-4): 230-236.

Rajaie, M., Ejraie, A.K., Owliaie, H.R. and Tavakoli, A.R. 2009. Effect of zinc and boron interaction on growth and mineral composition of lemon seedlings in a calcareous soil. *International Journal of Plant Production*, **3**(1): 39-50.

Rajput, C.B.S, Singh, B.P. and Mishra, H.P. 1976. Effects of foliar application of boron on mango. *Scientia Horticulturae*, **5**: 311-313.

Ramezani, S., Shekafandeh, A. and Taslimpour, M.R. 2010. Effect of GA_3 and zinc sulfate on fruit yield and oil percentage of 'Shengeh' olive trees. *International Journal of Fruit Science*, **10**(3): 228-234.

Rajak, U., Rani, R., Kumar, R., Mandal, B.K. and Prasad, K.K. 2010. Response of foliar mineral nutrition on bearing of mango cv Amrapali. *Environment and Ecology*, **28**(3): 1672-1675.

Rallo, L. and Suarez, M.P. 1989. Seasonal distribution of dry matter within the olive fruit bearing limb. *Advances in Horticultural Science*, **3**: 55-59.

Ramteke, S.D. and Somkumar, R.G. 2005. Effect of cycocel sprays on growth and yield of Tas-A-Ganesh grapes grafted on Dogridge rootstock. *Karnataka journal of Agricultural Science*, **18**(1): 18-20.

Rath,S. and Das,G.C. 1979. Effect of ringing and growth retardants on growth and flowering of mango. *Scientia Horticulturae*, **10**(1): 101-104.

Rath, S., Singh, R.L., Singh, B. and Singh, D.B. 1980. Effect of boron and zinc sprays on the physico-chemical composition of mango fruits. *The Punjab Horticultural Journal*, **20**: 33-35.

Rath, S. Das, G.C. and Singh, R.L. 1982. Manipulation of flowering in mango by forcing the dormant buds. *Bangladesh Horticulture*, **10**(1): 39-41.

Ravishankar, H., Nalawadi, V. G., Nulamani, N. C. 1993. Use of growth regulators to manipulate alternate bearing rhythm in mango (*Mangifera indica* L.). *Karnataka Journal of Agricultural Sciences*, **6**(1): 7-12.

Reddy, Y.T.N. and Kurian, R.M. 2008. Cumulative and residual effects of paclobutrazol on growth, yield and fruit quality of 'Alphonso' mango. *Journal of Horticultural Sciences*, **3**(2): 119-122.

Rivas, F., Martinez, F.A., Mesejo, C., Reig, C. and Agusti, M. 2010. Girdling effect on fruitlets hormonal and nutritional content in different Citrus shoot types. *Agrociencia Montevideo*, **14**(1): 8-14

Rufat, J. and Arbones, A. 2006. Foliar applications of boron to almond trees in dryland areas. *Acta Horticulturae*, **721**: 219-225.

Ryugo K. 1988. Fruit culture. It's Science and Art. John Wiley and Sons. p.259-261.

Saini, P. and Sharma, N. 2010. Effect of plant bio-regulators and evaporative cooling on fruit set, yield and quality of plum (*Prunus salicina* Lindl.) cv. Red Beaut. *Progressive Horticulture*, **42**(2): 220-223.

Sandhu, A. S., Singh, K., Mann, S. S. and Grewal, G. P. S. 1994. Influence of sources of zinc on growth and nutrient status of sand pear (*Pyrus pyrifolia* Nakai). *Acta Horticulturae*, **367**: 323-328.

Salazar-Garcia, S. and Vazquez, V. V. 1997. Physiological persistence of paclobutrazol on the "Tommy Atkins" mango (*Mangifera indica* L.) under rainfed conditions. *Journal of Horticultural Science*, **72**(2): 339-345.

Sanghavi, K.U. 1966. Effects of certain mechanical and chemical treatments on the improvement in the quality of Bhokri and Italian Elequina varieties of grape (*Vitis vinifera* L.). M. Sc. (Agric.) thesis, Poona University, Pune.

Sansavini, S., Cristoferi, G. and Montalti, P. 1988. Effects of paclobutrazol on growth, fruiting, carbohydrate metabolism in pear trees. *Advances in Horticultural Science*, **2**(2): 52-57.

Sarowa, P.S. and Bakshi, J.C. 1972. Fruit crops and quality regulation in Perlette veriety of *Vitis vinifera* grapes. IV. Effect of pruning, bunch thinning, girdling, sevin and gibberellic acid treatments. *The Punjab Horticultural Journal*, **12**(2-3): 68-77.

Sehrawat, S.K., Daulta, B.S., Dahiya, D.S. and Bhardwaj, R. 1998. Effect of growth retardants on growth, yield and fruit quality in grape (*Vitis vinifera* L.) cv. Thompson Seedless. *International Journal of Tropical Agriculture*, **16**(1/4): 179-184.

Sestak, Z., Carskry, J. and Jarvis, P.G. 1971. Plant photosynthetic production – Manual of methods. Dr. W. Junk, NY Publication, The Hague.

Sharma, A.K., Singh, K. and Mishra, S.P. 2003. Effect of foliar spray of zinc sulphate, 2,4,5-T and GA_3 on quality of kagzi lime (*Citrus aurantifolia* Swingle). *The Orissa Journal of Horticulture*, **31**(2): 29-32.

Sharma, N., Singh, K and Thakur, A. 2011. Effect of growth retardants on morphological, anatomical, physiological and fruiting characteristics of olives (*Olea europea* L.) under water stress conditions. *Acta Horticulturae*, **890**: 393-402.

Sharma, Y.M., Rathore, G.S. and Jesani, J.C. 1999. Effect of soil and foliar application of zinc and copper on yield and fruit quality of seedless lemon (*Citrus limon*). *Indian Journal of Agricultural Science*, **69**(3): 236-238.

Shishanku, G. V. and Titova, N. V. 1992. Effect of micro elements on photosynthetic productivity of peach trees. *Siinte Biologice si Chimice*, **6**: 21-25.

Shorrocks, V.M. 1997. The occurrence and correction of boron deficiency. *Plant and Soil*, **193**: 121-148.

Singh, K. and Khan, A. 1993. Effect of fertilization on yield and quality of mango fruit cv. Dashehari. *Progressive Horticulture*, **22**(1-4): 44-50.

Singh, B. and Rethy, P. 1996. Effect of certain micronutrients and NAA on the yield of Kagzi lime (*Citrus aurantifolia* Swingle). *Advances in Horticulture and Forestry*, **5**: 43-49.

Singh, D.B. and Ranganath, H.R. 2006. Induction of regular and early fruiting in mango by paclobutrazol under tropical humid climate. *Indian Journal of Horticulture*, **63**(3): 248-250.

Singh, V.K. and Bhattacherjee, A.K. 2005. Genotypic response of mango yield to persistence of paclobutrazol in soil. *Scientia Horticulturae*, **106**: 53-59.

Singh,N.P,. Malhi,C.S., Sharma,R.C. 2005. Effect of plant bio regulators (PBRs) on flowering, fruit yield and quality in mango cv. Dashehari. *Horticultural Journal*, **18**(1): 10-12.

Singh, N. and Chanana, Y.R. 2007. Effect of paclobutrazol and spacing on growth and yield of Shan-e-Punjab cv. of peach. *Indian Journal of Horticulture*, **64**(4): 456-458.

Singh, R. N. and Sharma, M. C. 1973. Response of young pear plants to growth retardants. *The Punjab Horticultural Journal*, **13**(2-3): 94-99.

Singh, R.R. 1977. Effect of various concentration of boron on growth characters and chemical composition of leaves of mango (*Mangifera indica* L.) cv. Langra. *Bangladesh Horticulture*, **5**(2): 30-34.

Singh, R. R. and Rajput, C. B. S. 1976. Effect of varying concentrations of zinc on vegetative growth characters, flowering, fruiting and physio-chemical composition of fruits in mango (*Mangifera indica* L.) cultivar Chausa. *Haryana Journal of Horticultural Sciences*, **5**(1-2): 10-14.

Singh, S. and Ahlawat, V. P. 1996. Effect of various concentrations of urea and zinc sulphate on vegetative growth of ber (*Zizyphus mauritiana* Lamk.) cv. Umran. *Haryana Journal of Horticultural Sciences*, **25** (1): 41-43.

Singh, B.P. and Singh, D. 1976. Effect of boron on vegetative growth characters and physico-chemical composition of Kagzi lime (*Citrus aurantifolia* Swingle). *Bangladesh Horticulture*, **4**(1): 29-31.

Singh, S. and Singh, A.K. 2006. Regulation of shoot growth and flowering in mango cv. Gulab Khas by paclobutrazol. *Annals of Agricultural Research*, **27**(1): 4-8.

Singh, V.K., Bhriguvanshi, S.R., and Chatterjee, C. 2009. Effect of micronutrients on growth and yield of mango (*Mangifera indica* L.) cv. Dashehari. *Asian Journal of Horticulture*, **4**(1): 112-115.

Singh, Z., Muller, W., Polesny, F., Verheyden, C. and Webster, A. D. 2000. Effect of (2 RS, 3 RS) paclobutrazol on tree vigour, flowering, fruit set and yield in mango. *Acta Horticulturae*, **525**: 459-462.

Sinha, M.M., Tripathi, S.P., Tewari, J.P. and Misra, R.S. 1983. Effect of alar and CCC on flowering and fruiting in peach cv. Alexander. *The Punjab Horticulture Journal*, **23**(1/2): 43-46.

Siqueira, D.L-de., Cecon, P.R. and Salomao, L.C.C. 2008. Growth of 'Volkameriano' lemmon tree treated with paclobutrazol and giberellic acid. *RevistaBrasileira de Fruticultura*, **30**(3): 764-768.

Skene, K.G.M. 1969. A comparison of the effects of cycocel and tipping on fruit set in *Vitis vinifera* L. *Australian Journal of Biological Sciences*, **22**: 1305-1311.

Soczek, Z. and Zaziabl, F. 1978. Response of two apple cvs. Jonathan and McIntosh to a long term application of retardants. *Fruit Science Reports*, **5**(3) 11-16.

Sotomayor, C., Silva, H. and Castro, J. 2000. Effectiveness of boron and zinc foliar sprays on fruit setting of two almond cultivars. *Acta Horticulturae*, **591**: 129-132.

Soyergin, S. 2010. Effects of soil and leaf treatments to eliminate boron deficiency in olives. *Communications in Soil Science and Plant Analysis*, **41**(16): 2004-2010.

Steffens, G.L. and Wang, S.Y. 1986. Biochemical and physiological alterations in apple trees caused by a gibberellins biosynthesis inhibitor, paclobutrazol. *Acta Horticulturae*, **179**: 433-442.

Stellacci, A.M., Caliandro, A., Mastro, M.A. and Guarini, D. 2010. Effect of Foliar Boron Application on Olive (*Olea europaea* L.) Fruit Set and Yield. *Acta Horticulturae*, **868**: 267-272.

Steyn, W.J., Ungerer, S.F. and Theron, K.I. 2008. Scoring and girdling, but not GA3. Increase yield without decreasing return bloom in 'Triumph' persimmon. *HortScience*, **43**(7): 2022-2026.

Stover, E., Fargione, M., Risio, R., Stiles, W. and Iungerman, K. 1999. Prebloom foliar boron, zinc, and urea applications enhance cropping of some 'Empire' and 'McIntosh' apple orchards in New York. *HortScience*, **34**(2): 210-214.

Subbiah, B.W. and Asija, G.L. 1956. A rapid procedure for the estimation of available nitrogen in soils. *Current Science*, **25**: 254-60.

Suryanarayana,V. 1981. A note on the effect of growth retardants on respiration and leaf pigments in mango. *South Indian Horticulture*, **29**(2): 117-119.

Suryanaranayana, V. and Rao, V. N. M. 1978. Effects of growth retardants on certain anatomical features of leaves in mango cultivar Mulgoa. *The Orissa Journal of Horticulture*, **6**(1-2): 17-20.

Svagzdys, S. 1995. Use of boron fertilizers in apple orchards of Lithuania. *Acta Horticulturae*, **383**: 487-490.

Swietlik, D. 1996. Responses of citrus trees in Texas to foliar and soil zinc applications. *Proceedings of International Society for Citriculture*, VIII International Citrus Congress, Sun City, South Africa, **2**: 772-776.

Swietlik, D. and Miller, S. S. 1985. The effect of paclobutrazol on mineral nutrition of apple seedlings. *Journal of Plant Nutrition*, **8**(5) : 369-382.

Swietlik, D. and LaDuke, J. 1991. Productivity, growth and leaf mineral composition of orange and grapefruit trees foliar-sprayed with zinc and manganese. *Journal of Plant Nutrition*, **14**: 129-142.

Syamal, M.M., Singh, S.K., Lal, H. and Singh, B.P. 2008. Effect of urea and zinc on growth, flowering, fruiting and fruit quality of kagzi lime (*Citrus aurantifolia* Swingle). *Environment and Ecology*, **26**(3): 1036-1038.

Taheri, M. and Talaie, A. 2001. The effect of chemical spray on the qualitative and quantitative characteristics of "Zard" olive fruits. *Acta Horticulturae*, **564**: 343-348.

Talaie, A. and Taheri, M. 2001. The effect of foliar spray with N, Zn and B on the fruit set and cropping of Iranian local olive trees. *Acta Horticulturae*, **564**: 337-341.

Tao, J.M., Sheng, B.C. and Zhang, F.S. 1998. Effects of chemical substances on shoot growth, fruit bearing, flower and fruit thinning of Fuji apple trees. *Advances in Horticulture*, **2**: 64-69.

Tariq, M., Sharif, M., Shah, Z. and Khan, R. 2007. Effect of foliar application of micronutrients on the yield and quality of sweet orange (*Citrus sinensis* L.). *Pakistan Journal of Biological Sciences*, **10**(11): 1823-1828.

Tesu, V., Toma, L.D. and Drobota, M.A. 1983. Effect of bioactive substances on growth and fruiting in pear. *Lucrari Stiintifice, Institutul Agronomic "Ion-Ionescu-de-la-Brad", Horticultura*, **27/28**: 79-80.

Thakur, S., Kumar, R., Sharma, K. K., Brahmchari, V. S., Chatterjee, D. and Kumar, R. 1989. Effect of different growth regulators on flowering characters of litchi (*Litchi chinensis* Sonn). *Orissa Journal of Horticulture*, **17**(1-2): 27-31.

Theron, K.Y., Plessis, P-du. and Griessel, M.M. 1998. Effect of autumn application of chlormequat on reproductive bud development, fruit set and production of the pear cv. Doyenne du Comice, Acta Horticulturae, 475: 251-264.

Thirugnanavel, A. Amutha, R., Rani, W.B., Indira, K., Mareeswari, P., Muthulakshmi, S. and Parthiban, S. 2007. Studies on regulation of flowering in acid lime (Citrus aurantifolia Swingle). Research Journal of Agriculture and Biological Sciences, 3(4): 239-241.

Tombesi, A., Boco, M., Pilli, M., and Farinelli, D. 2002a. Influence of canopy density on efficiency of trunk shaker on olive mechanical harvesting. *Acta Horticulturae*, **586**: 291-294.

Tukey, L. D. 1983. Vegetative control and fruiting on mature apple trees treated with PP333. *Acta Horticulturae*, **137**: 103-109.

Ungerer, S.F. and Steyn, W.J. 2009. Effect of scoring and GA$_3$ application during full bloom on fruit set and yield in 'Triumph' Persimmon. *Acta Horticulturae*, **833**: 207-211.

Vavilov, N.I. 1951. Phytogeographic basis of plant breeding. The origin, variation, immunity and breeding of cultivated plants. *Chronica Botanica*, **13**: 1-364.

Vejendla, V., Maity, P.K., Banik, B.C. 2008. Effect of chemicals and growth regulators on fruit retention, yield and quality of mango cv. Amrapali. *Journal of Crop and Weed*, **4**(2): 45-46.

Wali, V.K., Kaul, R. and Kher, R. 2005. Effect of foliar sprays of nitrogen, potassium and zinc on yield and physic-chemical composition of phalsa (*Grewia subinaequalis* DC) cv. Purple Round. *Haryana Journal of Horticultural Science*, 34 (1-2): 56-57.

Walworth, J.L., Pond, A.P., Sower, G.J., and Kilby, M.W. 2006. Fall applied foliar zinc for pecans. *HortScience*, **41**(1): 275-76.

Wang, S.P., Jia, H.J., Gao, Z.J. and Wang, S.Z. 1993. Study on PP333 application to the growth and development of young peach tree. *Acta Horticulturae Sinica*, **20**(2): 139-144.

Wargo, J.M., Merwin, I.A. and Watkin, C.B. 2004. Nitrogen fertilization, midsummer trunk girdling, and AVG treatments affect maturity and quality of 'Jonagold' apple. *HortScience*, **39**: 493-500.

Werner, H. 1993. Influence of paclobutrazol on growth and leaf nutrient content of mango (cv. Blanco). *Acta Horticulturae*, **341**: 225-231.

West, C., Briggs, G.E., and Kidds, F. 1920. Methods and significant relations in the quantitative analysis of plant growth. *New Phytologia*, **19**: 200-207.

Westwood, M.N. 1978. Temperate Zone Pomology, W.H. Freeman Co. San Francisco California, pp. 428.

Williams, M. W. 1973. Chemical control of vegetative growth and flowering in apple trees. *Acta Horticulturae*, **34** : 167-173.

Wojcik, P. 1998. Effect of boron fertilization on growth, yield and fruit quality of plum trees. *Acta Horticulturae*, **478**: 255-260.

Wojcik, P. and Mika, A. 1996. Effect of fertilization of apple trees with boron on the growth, yield and fruit quality. *Zeszyty-Problemowe-Postepow-Nauk-Rolniczych*, **434**(I): 419-424.

Wojcik, P., Cieslinski, G. and Mika, A. 1999. Apple yield and fruit quality as influenced by boron applications. *Journal of Plant Nutrition*, **22**(9): 1365-1377.

*Wu, S.Z., Yang, Z. G., Wung, L. S., Wu, S. Y. and Zheng, S. D. 2000. Effects of spraying PP333 for nodulating the blossom period. *China Fruits*, **4**: 30-31.

Yadava, R.B.R. and Singh, V.K. 1998. Long term effects of paclobutrazol (PP333) on yield and quality of dashehari mango (*Mangifera indica* L.). *Indian Journal of Plant Physiology*, **3**(2): 166-167.

Yadav, R.K., Rana, G.S., Ahlawat, V.P., Dahiya, D.S. and Kumar, S. 2007. Effect of zinc application on growth and fruit drop of sweet orange (*Citrus sinensis* Osbeck) cv. Jaffa. *Haryana Journal of Horticultural Science*, **36**(3/4): 205-206.

Yadav, S., Shukla, H.S. and Ram, R.A. 2010. Studies on foliar application of NAA, GA$_3$, boric acid, and Ca(NO$_3$)$_2$ on fruit retention, growth, yield and quality of aonla (*Emblica officinalis* Gaertn.) cv. Banarsi. *The Horticulture Journal*, **23**(2): 64-67

*Yamamoto, S. 1983. Studies on the growing of loquat in a vinyl green house. I. Effect of plant growth regulators and physical treatment on the young trees an on the appearance of flower clusters. *Bulletin of the Faculty of Agriculture-Miyazaki University*, **30**(2): 243-253.

Zhu, L.H., Li, M.L. and Cao, Q.C. 1994. The influence of paclobutrazol on walnut trees. *Forest Research*, **7**(1): 33-37.

Zude, M., Alexander, A. and Ludders, P. 1998. Influence of boron spray in autumn or spring on flower boron concentration, fruit set and yield in apple cv. Elstar. *Erwerbsobstbau*, **40**(1): 18-21.

www.ingramcontent.com/pod-product-compliance
Lightning Source LLC
Chambersburg PA
CBHW020219290326
41948CB00001B/100